"You don't know anything about me,"

she warned with a tremor in her voice. "I . . . could have done something . . . terrible."

He grinned disbelievingly down at her. "I'll bet you've never even had a parking ticket." He paused, watching her face closely for her reaction, then spoke softly, his voice dropping intimately. "I'd also bet there have been few men in your bed."

His words had an immediate and dizzying effect, followed by a rush of something so inexplicable coursing through her that it unnerved her completely and left her feeling naked and vulnerable.

"You shouldn't talk to me like this," she murmured.

"Shouldn't I?" he replied, looking completely unrepentant as his marauding gaze slid over her face. "By now you must realize the effect you have on me."

Dear Reader:

We at Silhouette are very excited to bring you a NEW reading **Sensation.** *Look out for the four books which will appear in our new Silhouette* **Sensation** *series every month. These stories will have the high quality you have come to expect from Silhouette, and their varied and provocative plots will encourage you to explore the wonder of falling in love – again and again!*

Emotions run high in these drama-filled novels. Greater sensual detail and an extra edge of realism intensify the hero and heroine's relationship so that you cannot help but be caught up in their every change of mood.

We hope you enjoy this new **Sensation** *– and will go on to enjoy many more.*

We would love to hear your comments about our new line and encourage you to write to us:

Jane Nicholls
Silhouette Books
PO Box 236
Thornton Road
Croydon
Surrey
CR9 3RU

JOANNA MARKS
Love is a Long Shot

Silhouette Sensation

First published in Great Britain in 1991 by Silhouette Books, Eton House, 18-24 Paradise Road, Richmond, Surrey TW9 1SR

© Joanna Darby 1989

Silhouette, Silhouette Sensation and Colophon are Trade Marks of Harlequin Enterprises B.V.

ISBN 0 373 58267 6

18 – 9109

Made and printed in Great Britain

Chapter 1

Laura looked out over the large illuminated office at Cranston Aviation. She had been working at the airfreight company for almost a year now, and it was beginning to feel like home. The thought filled her with a warm contented glow as she leaned against the front of her desk, cautiously sipping hot coffee.

In the hangar adjoining the glass wall that partitioned off the office, mechanics crawled over the bodies of two DC3s being checked out for their next flights. The DC3, Laura had discovered since working here, was one of the most reliable airplanes ever built and still in operation all over the world despite its age.

Mr. Barnes, her boss, walked into the hangar, alongside a lean, broad-shouldered man. The man stood with his back to Laura so that she couldn't see his face, and she noticed him in that half-seeing, slightly distracted way one studies some distant object and fails to really see it. Her thoughts were on other things, namely, the taupe coat with the silver-fox collar she had seen on sale in Gibson's. It was absolutely gorgeous and had a price tag that took her breath away. Laura did some swift, mad calculations, but no matter how she juggled her bank account and her future paychecks, the figures didn't come out right and she knew she couldn't really afford the coat. Nor could she justify the expense, since Florida had only a few weeks of really cold weather each winter that warranted a warm coat. With a small sigh of resignation, she took another cautious sip of the steaming coffee.

Something the unknown man did caught her attention, and she began to study him more carefully. He wore a deep brown leather flying jacket and dark pants that outlined lean hips and long legs. His thick dark hair had been ruffled by the cold March winds. Probably a candidate for a job. Laura knew Mr. Barnes was looking for a new pilot. One of his older pilots had developed a heart condition and had had to leave suddenly. A commercial cargo airline short of pilots meant delays and disgruntled customers. Mr. Barnes would be desperate to replace him, she was sure of that.

Still thinking how wonderful she would feel in the taupe coat with the fur collar turned up around her face, Laura noted idly that the stranger was a tall man. He towered over short, stocky Mr. Barnes, and moved with an effortless grace. As Laura's gaze lingered, a nameless unease started to uncoil inside her.

The taupe coat went instantly and completely out of her mind. She stood transfixed, watching everything he did, waiting for him to turn so that she could catch a glimpse of his face. His head was angled downward as he listened to Mr. Barnes, who was pointing to the nearest aircraft. She saw the man lift a hand and unzip his leather flying jacket, but his back was still toward her and she couldn't see his face. Having unzipped his jacket, he slid his hands to his hips and rested them there, pushing the jacket back out of the way. Then some noise, perhaps a mechanic dropping a wrench, a drill suddenly switched on, made him turn his dark head and she saw the side of his face.

She stood stunned, unable to believe what her senses told her. Her mind reacted with denial. Don't panic! Keep calm. The sharp commands echoed in her head in quick succession. It was just someone who looked like him. The eyes could play tricks on perception, everybody knew that.

She placed the coffee cup down on the desk with a tremulous hand. Her protective instincts sent her thoughts darting from one possibility to another, from one explanation to another, frantically trying to explain away the man in the hangar who had suddenly sprung into her life from out of the past. A past she thought she had buried deep inside. A past that her conscious mind had successfully wallpapered over with the humdrum patterns of everyday life. She had pretended for some time now that it had never happened, had convinced herself that it had been nothing but a bad dream, some mirage her overactive imagination had conjured up. Now all those carefully constructed lies and deceptions were being stripped away by the appearance of this stranger. She could not still the searing apprehension that filled her, nor quiet her jangled nerves as dark thoughts converged, jolting her to the alarming possibilities that stranger's presence presented.

She would just sit down a moment and not get into a flap, she told herself, struggling for calm. Then she would quietly and inconspicuously get up and go to the rest room to wash her hands and give herself another few minutes to compose her thoughts with no one else around. She sat and waited and finally saw Mr. Barnes turn away from the man and walk toward the door that joined his office to the hangar area. The other man had disappeared from her view to another part of the hangar. She looked up as she felt Mr. Barnes's gaze upon her. He signaled to her to come into his office. She moved away from her desk and walked toward the glass enclosure. Once inside, she stood in front of his desk, trying to still the pounding of her heart.

"We've got a new pilot working for us, Laura." He beamed, pleased with himself at having filled the vacancy. "I want you to type up his personal data and file it. There's something I want to tell you about him, but I haven't got the time right now. I'll speak to you about it later."

"Yes, Mr. Barnes," she replied softly, taking the papers he held out. She didn't trust herself to look at them, and she tried to keep her visibly shaking hand still, thrusting it, with the papers, to her side.

"That's all for now, Laura." He smiled kindly. She smiled back, thinking once again how lucky she was to have Mr. Barnes as her employer. He had always treated her like one of his own daughters, and she loved working for him. She would hate to have to leave Cranston. She was jumping to hasty wild conclusions, she told herself as she turned away and moved back across the carpeted, plant-lined office area to her desk. She sat down, placing the folder in front of her. It looked harmless enough. Just a simple manila folder with an application form inside it, the necessary information required of any new employee. That was all it was. Harmless, perfectly harmless.

Look at it, her mind ordered. Simply pick it up and look at it. Go on. Look at it.

With trembling hands, she opened the folder and forced herself to read the application form. Then her heart stopped beating, and her breath stayed lodged in her throat somewhere. His name bounced wildly off the page. She shut her eyes as the words danced in her mind's eye, causing fear to splinter through her entire being. Questions crowded into her mind in a silent barrage that she was unable to answer. She opened her eyes and forced herself to look again at the application in front of her.

Quinton Jones. Male. Caucasian. Thirty-four years old. University of Central Florida. U.S. Air Force Academy. The words began to swim in front of her eyes; her mind barely able to absorb what she was reading. She scanned the list of previous employers and noticed a gap, several years that had been left carefully blank, unaccounted for.

All the blood drained from her face, and she put a shaky hand to her head to conceal her expression from anybody who happened to be looking her way. It was him, there was no doubt about it. What was she going to do? Would it be possible to avoid him? Maybe he would never see her. The pilots came into the office to check on inventories of goods, to talk with Mr. Barnes about changes in routes, any last-minute hitches because of the weather or to discuss some mechanical delay. No! That was a desperate, foolish hope. It was impossible to avoid him. Sooner or later he would see her. That was a certainty.

Frantically she reminded herself that she had been only sixteen at the time. Her appearance had changed dramatically since then. She had been an unsophisticated adolescent, a real Plain Jane. She had even worn glasses. Her hair had been pulled back, secured by an elastic band. She reached up to touch the mane of golden-chestnut curls that now framed the mature contours of her face. The up-to-the-minute hairstyle and deftly applied makeup had transformed her completely. She was taller now, too, and her willowy figure had filled out in all the right places. Yes, to even the most discerning eyes she would be completely unrecognizable from her former self, from that timid sixteen-year-old girl. Yes, she thought, relaxing, there was every chance he would not recognize her. She had even changed her name. What a lucky decision that had been. She had done it because she wanted to put the past behind her, to start fresh, so she had legally changed it. She was no longer the Cathy Turner he'd known at the trial. She had taken her grandmother's maiden name, Reynolds, and used her own middle name, Laura. She almost laughed out loud with relief, because she had grown so accustomed to her new name she had almost forgotten she hadn't always had it.

A movement in her peripheral vision caught Laura's attention. She turned her head and saw her friend Tina Rivera walking toward her. Smiling, Laura quickly masked her anxiety.

With her usual air of camaraderie, Tina perched on the edge of Laura's desk and bent forward, a mischievous glimmer in her dark eyes.

"Barnes just hired a new pilot," Tina whispered. "And is he a hunk! Have you seen him?"

"I haven't gotten a good look at him. I've only seen him from a distance. Barnes gave me his paperwork. I was about to type it up." Her words came out faster than usual, betraying her edginess.

"Well if you get the chance, find some excuse to go out into the hangar. He's still out there talking to one of the mechanics. That is, if you want to be positively bowled over by sheer masculinity and sex appeal that oozes from every pore. Of course, if you're not impressed by that sort of thing," Tina said, studying her fingernail polish with exaggerated interest, "I won't hold it against you, because I would like a clear field, actually."

"If he's all you say he is, he's out of my league," Laura murmured. Tina's interest in Quint could be an advantage. Laura didn't want anyone, including Tina, to think that she was at all interested. She was determined to keep a low profile and fade into the background.

Unfortunately, her ploy backfired, because Tina's antennae went up instantly. Her gaze slipped over Laura's curving figure, long legs, green eyes and mop of golden brown curling hair. "You're underestimat-

ing your charms," she said. "Why is that, I wonder?"

Tina was too quick, Laura thought. She should have
known better. The last thing she wanted was Tina to
have any suspicions regarding her and Quint Jones.

With studied casualness she replied, "I . . . have my
eye on someone else at the moment. Besides, I hav-
en't gotten a really good look at him yet." She smiled
sweetly trying to cover up her anxiety again. There was
no one in her life at the moment, but she would invent somebody if necessary.

Tina smiled back with good-natured delight at her
reply.

"Thanks. I'll remember you in my will." She slid
off the desk and turned back toward her own desk.

As Laura watched her go, a soft sigh of relief escaped. That was one tricky situation out of the way.
Was this how it was going to be from now on? Her
head and mind reeled.

Her gaze flickered back to the application. Marital
status: Single. Address: 326 Cherry Street. She wondered if he lived alone, if he had made any friends
since he had served his time. They said getting back
into the world was immensely difficult.

She closed her eyes, squeezing them tightly shut as
remorse eddied inside her. It wasn't all her fault, she
told herself. It wasn't all her fault. She had to remember that. She couldn't help it. She'd only been sixteen, good grief, she couldn't forget that.

Laura slipped some paper into the typewriter and
began typing a formal file on him with all the necessary data, forcing herself to concentrate, forcing herself to forget for a moment. Until she finished this, she

promised herself she wouldn't think about it. She had a job to do. She couldn't indulge herself in emotional drama. She was a working girl with bills to pay, dependent on her own earnings. There was no room for reflection on anything else.

She started typing.

When she looked up at the clock again, it was nearly five o'clock. She tidied her desk and slipped her handbag out of the drawer. She slid her coat off the hanger in the closet, pulled it on and waved goodbye to Tina and Mr. Barnes across the space of the office. She hurried out of the building into the cool evening. The sky rumbled ominously, and she knew that it would pour any minute.

The rain began to spatter down as she walked briskly across the parking lot. It crossed her mind that she should stop and get something for dinner at the nearby supermarket, but the sanctuary of her apartment beckoned so strongly that she decided to make do with the leftovers in the refrigerator. She slid into the front seat of her car and searched her handbag for her keys.

The traffic was heavy on the way home, and the rain pelted down on the windshield so hard the wipers couldn't keep up with it. The drive home was a slow one; she had too much time to think, too much time to remember.

When she reached her apartment she flung her coat onto the nearest chair and walked into the kitchen to take some aspirin out of the cupboard. Her head throbbed painfully. She swallowed the aspirin and closed her eyes, waiting for the relief to come to her pounding temples. In her bedroom, she stripped off her clothes, dropping them heedlessly on the floor behind her, and walked into the shower. Immediately the warm soothing spray pelted down on her soft skin. The water streamed down the walls of the cubicle and over her. The mist of the spray hung in the air as she languished underneath it, closing her eyes and trying to dispel the images that crowded into her mind. She pressed her hands to her temples trying to squeeze the images out, but they kept flashing in relentless and devastating succession, like the images in an old-fashioned nickelodeon machine.

Finally she could suppress them no longer and she began to sob, little tiny muffled sounds at first that gradually escalated into great racking sobs that were soundless but heart wrenching, and they went on and on until she could cry no more.

The next morning her eyes were red and swollen. She used an astringent and bathed them repeatedly to get the swelling down, and then she summoned up all her skill as she applied her makeup, trying to disguise the ravages of the night before. As she slid into a two-piece outfit with a fitted black-and-white houndstooth-check jacket and pencil slim black skirt, she gazed at herself in the mirror, trying to restore her confidence. She purposely kept her hair in its tousled casual curling style because it was so completely different from the way it had been at the trial. Now it framed the delicate contours of her face, emphasizing her green eyes. She reassessed her changed physical appearance to reassure herself and calm her jangled nerves. She tried to remember exactly how tall she had been at sixteen. She glanced down at her high-heeled pumps. That was another thing in her favor. It was a small thing, but she breathed more deeply and felt more confident somehow.

When she reached the office, she noticed that Mr. Barnes was already at his desk. She immediately began sorting through some work she wanted to file away before he called her in. On edge, she knew he would want to speak to her first thing this morning, and her instincts told her it was about Quint. After about fifteen minutes, he signaled to her through the glass partition. She immediately picked up a notepad and pencil and walked in.

"Good morning, Mr. Barnes." She tried to appear as normal as possible.

"For heaven's sake, when are you going to learn to call me Jim, like everybody else, Laura?"

She hesitated and blushed. Perhaps it was out of respect for his age. His first name always stuck in her throat and "Mr. Barnes" rolled off her tongue so much more easily than "Jim."

"It's just a habit I got into," she apologized, a little embarrassed. "That's how I think of you. You're always Mr. Barnes in my mind."

"Okay," he said good-naturedly.

She could see that he really didn't mind. She thought it secretly pleased him.

"Now that you mention it, I think I would find it strange if you did start calling me Jim." He turned over some papers on his desk and then looked back up at her.

"I wanted to talk to you about the new pilot I hired," he said, rolling back in his swivel chair and bracing his elbows on the arms to steeple his hands in front of his face.

"You're not a gossipy girl, Laura. At least from what I've seen of you, you don't strike me as that type. What I have to tell you is between you and me, and I don't want it to go any further. I think I can trust you to keep it under your hat, can't I?" His blue eyes held a silent appeal.

"Yes," she murmured, looking at him directly. Yes, most certainly. If he only knew, she would be the last person in the world to want to gossip about Quint. She struggled not to let the inner turmoil that his words were stirring up show on her face.

"Good. Our new pilot—I gave you his paperwork yesterday. Not all his data is filled in. There are one or two things we have to adjust, gloss over for his sake. One of them is that he has served time in prison." His gaze flickered up to hers to judge her reaction.

She tried to keep her gaze steady and not blink an eye.

"I see," she said quietly.

"So we're going to make a few minor adjustments; invent something for his previous employer, fix the dates, how long he worked there, et cetera. And keep it to yourself. Have I made myself clear?"

"Perfectly," she murmured.

"I believe a man deserves a second chance. Don't you?"

She nodded, not trusting herself to speak.

"I can see your heart is in the right place, Laura. He does seem to be a good man. It's really hard to believe that he's an ex-con." He stared at some point in the distance unseeingly, then back at her.

"When you meet him, you'll see what I mean. He doesn't act like the sort of man who would be found guilty of manslaughter, or any serious charge for that matter.''

Laura stood in rigid silence, unable to move, unable to speak.

''Ah, well, that's life,'' he said, unsteepling his hands. ''We've all got skeletons in our closets, things we've done…enough said. You'll fix that, Laura, and remember, not a word to anyone. He's paid his debt to society as far as I'm concerned.''

As Laura stood in rigid silence, her mind raced. Mr. Barnes had said the man deserved a second chance. A second chance. Did she deserve a second chance? Would he give her a second chance? She didn't think so.

She murmured an almost incoherent reply to Mr. Barnes and turned quickly away, wanting very much to get back to the relative safety of her desk.

Her head was spinning, and there seemed to be nothing she could do to stop it. Mechanically she picked up the application and filled in his last employer as Drake Airlines, to satisfy any prying eyes that happened upon it. Position Held: Pilot. When she came to salary she put down one that she knew was in keeping with what a pilot with a small airline would have earned. Her fingers moved in a jerky fashion over the typewriter keys, and eventually she settled down into something vaguely resembling her usual efficiency. She closed her eyes periodically and prayed to get through the day. If she could just get through this day she told herself, tomorrow would be easier and the day after that even easier until, by the end of the week, she should be back to something resembling normal.

When she finally looked up from her work she saw Tina strolling toward her desk with her usual air of joie de vivre. As usual, she perched on the edge of Laura's desk.

"Aren't we serious today! Did something go wrong with what's-his-name? You seem to have a black cloud suspended over you."

Laura summoned up a hasty smile to dispel that impression. "No, I just stayed up too late reading, and now I'm feeling a bit jaded. I didn't get enough sleep, that's all."

"Have you see him yet?" Tina tilted her head in the direction of the hangar.

"No," Laura replied absentmindedly. Sooner or later it was going to happen, and she wasn't at all sure what she was going to do or how she was going to react. The prospect shook her, and it must have shown in her face.

"Don't let him get you down," Tina said softly. Laura looked up startled.

"What's-his-name, don't let him get you down. If things are going wrong, just remember there are lots of other fish in the sea." Laura was instantly relieved as she realized Tina was referring to the invented man in her life and not Quint Jones.

"But don't go fishing for that one out there." Tina motioned to the hangar again. "He belongs to me. That's if he will let me catch him." She bent forward. "Fill me in on the details."

"What details?"

"His vital statistics, of course. Is he single, divorced? He doesn't have a married look. I hope I'm not mistaken."

"No," Laura said quickly, increasingly glad that Tina might serve as a distraction and aid in preventing her from being detected. "You've got a clear field. It says single on his application. Unless he's got a fiancée tucked away somewhere. And he's well educated. But how do you propose to meet him? Will you get Barnes to introduce you, or will you invent some excuse to go out there?"

"Trust me, darling, I'll think of something. Feminine wiles are inexhaustible, you know."

She slid off the desk. "I'd better go and do some work."

Laura's gaze followed her, then drifted back toward the hangar, and then she turned to her work.

Later in the afternoon, Mr. Barnes signaled frantically to her to come into his office. When she reached the glassed-in partition that separated him from the rest of the office staff, he looked up with a harassed expression on his face.

"Laura, will you make these adjustments? Customers that call up at the last minute and expect you to move heaven and earth for them drive me up the wall."

Laura watched him disappear into the hangar. She picked up the lists and studied them intently, dismayed by all the last-minute changes. She knew she'd have to get busy making the adjustments on the computer if she wanted to do a printout quickly enough.

Completely absorbed, she didn't hear the outer door to Mr. Barnes's office open and close softly. With her gaze still locked on the lists, she swung around and suddenly slammed into a solid wall of rock-hard flesh.

Startled, she gasped and jumped back as the cargo lists flew from her hand and fluttered to the floor.

"Oh, damn it," she muttered, reaching down to pick up the sheaves of paper. When she looked up, she was horrified to find herself staring into the wary gray eyes of Quint Jones. His stunning good looks plunged her into momentary speechlessness. The force of his tough, masculine presence seemed to crowd the small office.

He didn't move a muscle as his eyes engaged hers with an almost hostile stare. Then with male thoroughness he let his gaze slide with lazy inspection over her.

Laura felt her face grow warm. Immediately, the sting of heady sensuality flared between them like a just-struck match, and then the equally powerful sting of fear followed quickly on its heels.

"I thought you heard me come in," he said with studied indifference.

His low, even voice eddied into her ear from some distant point in space, jolting her out of her momentary stunned state. He was speaking to her. His quizzical expression indicated he found her slightly demented and not all there. She summoned up her voice.

"I...d-didn't hear you," she murmured, stammering like a schoolgirl. "I...uh...was concentrating on these lists," she added. Her voice and face mirrored her confusion as she pointed to the papers on the floor. She had to get away from him.

Hastily she bent to retrieve the remainder of the scattered lists, searching for any excuse to move away and not have to look him in the eye. The question *does he remember?* surged and hovered uppermost in her mind.

"Wait a minute. I'll help you," he said quietly. With the same effortless grace she had noticed before, he bent down beside her. His tall, leanly muscled frame was barely an inch away now. His shoulder grazed her arm, his muscular thigh almost touching hers. Her heart pounded wildly as he helped her gather the papers.

He regarded her with lazy amusement. "Do you bump into people a lot?" He flashed a teasing smile that softened his stern features.

"Not a lot." She laughed nervously.

"I suppose I should have said something." His smile slipped away, and he was guarded once again, so self-contained that she could detect nothing of what was going on behind those amazing gray eyes that had changed from silver to leaden and had become suddenly veiled and remote. If he recognized her, there was still no outward sign that he did. The thought calmed her, and she looked down at the papers again and began to rise slowly, not looking at him.

"That might not be a bad idea," she said with a flirtatious note in her voice that was remarkable, considering the circumstances.

She straightened to her full height and gave the papers another little juggle to align the edges. She was acutely aware of his nearness, of him standing over her, and she was glad to have something to do with her hands for a brief moment. She knew that she had to look up at him, look him in the face again or it would seem odd. Summoning up a fair imitation of a relaxed smile, she slowly lifted her eyes to meet his

steady gaze. There was something about his nearness
that made her hand shake involuntarily, and she almost dropped the lists all over again. Instantly, she
attempted to cover up the potent effect he had on her.

"You must be the new pilot, Quint Jones. Wel-
come to Cranston Aviation. I'm Laura Reynolds."

"Thanks," he said, still watching her warily. The
ghost of a smile touched the corners of his mouth.

"Mr. Barnes is a great guy. Everybody likes working for him," she added.

He was studying her silently again. Perhaps he was
wondering if she knew about him. He probably wondered that about anyone he met, she thought. But her
friendly manner seemed to satisfy him.

"I hope I will, too," he replied with a kind of cynical reserve. Her heart clenched at the distance he put
between himself and those around him, the hard suspicious wall he seemed to have built around himself,
as if he were forever waiting for someone or something to attack him. Her gaze flickered as she realized
that she had been partly responsible for putting it
there.

"I've got to be getting back to my desk. I've got
plenty to do. It was nice meeting you," she said quietly, the trite phrase almost choking her.

"Nice meeting you," he replied. He was still studying her with the same intent look in his gray eyes, as if
he could see into the very depths of her soul. Feeling
his gaze following her, she turned away, practically
gasping for air, as if the shock of seeing him, being so
close to him, had stopped her from breathing.

She didn't realize just how stunned she was from
this surprise encounter with Quint Jones until she be-

gan walking briskly back toward her desk. She barely felt her feet moving across the carpet. It was as if her legs belonged to someone else, but somehow she was moving along on them anyway. Her breathing was shallow and quick. A soft sheen of perspiration began to explode onto her forehead.

Had he recognized her? She didn't think so. She hoped that she hadn't made much of an impression on him. She hoped that from here on in she could fade into the background and if he thought of her at all, it would be as part of the office furniture.

Later in the week she saw him several times, going into Mr. Barnes's office, picking up flight schedules, checking on one thing or another. Her gaze would furtively follow him, and she was careful that no one saw her watching. She could tell from Mr. Barnes's manner that he liked his new pilot.

It was after one of these brief visits by Quint that Mr. Barnes called Laura into his office. As he was passing her some schedules to be typed, he commented, "I'm really pleased with Quint Jones. He's an excellent pilot, and he seems to know almost as much about airplane engines as some of my mechanics." Through Mr. Barnes's partition, Laura could see Quint talking to one of the mechanics apparently about a fuselage repair job. The only people she ever saw him talking to were the mechanics, she suddenly realized.

Her gaze swung sideways to Tina's desk. Tina was talking to one of the other secretaries. Laura doubted that Tina had been able to make much progress at all where Quint was concerned.

Mr. Barnes seemed to be waiting for some kind of response from her.

"He looks like a good man. No matter what has been in his past," she said. Mr. Barnes nodded in agreement.

That was the least she could do for Quint, Laura thought. Vouch for him now, show confidence in him. The very least. She wished she could do more. She wished that somehow she could put it right, but she knew that any attempt in that direction would be foolhardy.

"That's exactly how I feel, Laura. Every time I come into contact with him, I feel it more strongly."

Laura smiled agreeably and picked up the time schedules, preparing to leave before they got any more involved in a conversation about Quint Jones.

Chapter 2

It was May. Laura stared at the calendar above her desk. Quint had been at Cranston's over two months, and they'd had little contact with each other. Occasionally she saw him in the canteen grabbing a cup of coffee and a snack. Once he was taxiing down the runway when she went out to tell Mr. Barnes he was wanted on the telephone. Then there were those brief occasions when Quint conferred with Mr. Barnes in his office.

Laura busied herself in her work and had relaxed into thinking they could go on this way indefinitely.

Tina slid out from behind her desk and sauntered across the office toward Laura. There was a distinct look of frustration in her dark eyes.

"Well, what's bothering you?" Laura asked.

"I've tried *everything* to get him to notice me,"

Tina announced with a flourish of her hands, indicating mock despair.

"Who?" Laura asked, knowing full well who she meant.

"You know very well who. Mr. Mystery Man, the Lone Ranger." She held out her hands palms up. "What does a girl have to do? Have I lost my charm? Are my looks fading? Tell me. Maybe it is better that I know."

"I don't think so," Laura said, smiling. "Maybe you should just write him off as the one that got away."

"No! He is a challenge, and it only makes him all the more interesting." Tina paused reflectively for a long moment. "You know, I've tried everything, simply everything. I've tried bumping into him at the coffee machine. I've flirted outrageously. I've used my most brilliant smile." She displayed beautiful white even teeth and batted her eyelashes provocatively. "I've introduced him to people, thinking, maybe, he was just a little shy, and I tried to draw him out. But that one is like a closed fortress. You can't get even close. I hate to admit it, but I even went out to the parking lot and let out the air out of one of my tires when I knew he would be passing my car on the way to his home." She looked down at Laura and rolled her eyes expressively. "Well, I was getting desperate."

"You didn't."

"I did," Tina replied, unabashed, but looking over her shoulder to make sure no one was listening.

Tina really had it bad, Laura decided as she listened with her head propped up by her hand. It was truly amazing the lengths the woman was willing to go to, in order to get Quint interested. Laura felt that Tina had made herself so obvious that she had ruined whatever chance she had, but she didn't want to say that to her friend.

"Maybe he's got a girlfriend somewhere and he's simply not interested in female company. He's satisfied with what he's got."

"My instincts tell me no," Tina maintained stubbornly. "He keeps himself so . . . apart. I think there's something about him. I don't know what it is. I can't put my finger on it exactly. There's something different about him."

Laura felt a tiny alarm bell going off in her mind. She didn't want Tina's suspicions aroused. She didn't want her to know about Quint's time in prison. It could be dangerous. Tina was not the most close-mouthed of people. She had many good points, but being discreet wasn't one of them.

"I think we should respect a person's privacy. Don't you? People have a right to keep themselves to themselves if they want to. If he wants to be so self-contained, like a fortress, as you put it, that's his business. Some people are awkward in social situations and it's a waste of time trying to force them to be what they simply cannot be."

"I go along with that. But he's not shy. I would bet my life on it. It's something else. I just don't know what." A puzzled frown creased her brow. "Have you seen him up close?"

"Yes." Laura studied her fingernails intently, not wanting to give away the devastating effect he'd had on her.

"Well! You're not going to tell me that you don't find him attractive!"

Laura had to agree. There was something about Quint Jones that set him apart. He exuded something dangerous. Only she wasn't quite sure what it was. There seemed to be a seething mass of emotions inside him that threatened to break the bounds of restraint. There was wariness about him that bordered on hostility. She pitied the person who unlocked the restraint, who unwittingly triggered the release. It would be folly to say that she didn't find him attractive. In spite of his suspicious demeanor, he had a strong sensual appeal that made women's heads turn, while his steely strength made men respect him.

"I think he is attractive," she replied finally.

"I just knew you were going to say that eventually." Tina sounded smug.

"But when you're interested in someone else, you tend not to pay too much attention," Laura added, trying again to cover up her attraction to Quint. "Besides, looks aren't everything."

"But he looks like he's got everything else as well." Tina laughed with irrepressible delight. "Jim says he's one of the best pilots he's ever had, et cetera, et cetera." She was like a hound dog that couldn't be shaken off a track once it had picked up the scent. Laura wished they could just drop the subject.

"What did he do when you did manage to speak to him at the coffee machine?" Laura asked, suddenly curious to know how Quint had reacted. "And what happened when he saw your flat tire?"

"Oh, he answered in monosyllables at the coffee machine. Not exactly encouraging when you're trying to strike up a friendly conversation. I don't think he spoke one complete sentence. And when he saw me struggling with the flat tire, he came over and asked if he could help. I said I would be very grateful if he would. He then went to work and finished in about ten minutes flat. I asked him if he would like to join me for a coffee. He made some polite excuse and disappeared off into the night. I think he managed one complete sentence that time." She frowned suddenly. "You don't think he's one of *those*, do you," she whispered conspiratorially.

"I wouldn't have thought so," Laura replied, amused.

"No, you're right. I guess I just have to face facts," Tina added glumly. "I don't seem to turn him on." She smoothed her tomato-red dress over her hips. Laura breathed a silent sigh of relief, glad that the conversation regarding Quint was coming to an end. Tina started to leave, then impulsively swung back around, black eyes flashing with sudden enthusiasm.

"Are you going to the picnic?"

"What picnic?"

"The Memorial Day picnic. It's *the* big annual event in this town. It's the only thing that ever happens here. They always have it in Five Lakes Park every year on a Sunday. The whole thing is financed by small businesses, the Chamber of Commerce, the American Legion, and so forth."

"I'll have to think about it," Laura said.

Tina's phone buzzed on her desk, and she rushed to the other side of the room to pick it up.

Laura plunged back into her work, pushing the picnic to the back of her mind and hoping that Tina would soon forget all about Quint Jones. She was completely absorbed, until a shadow fell across her desk. With a sense of unease sliding through her, she raised her gaze slowly to meet Quint Jones's wintry, fathomless eyes. She was unable to hide the quick response. He walked like a jungle cat, she thought, as her breath seemed to jam painfully in her chest and that strange breathless sensation attacked her again.

"Either I seem to be making a habit of taking you by surprise or you're the jumpiest woman I ever met," he said in a low, mocking voice.

He stood towering over her, his hands shoved into the pockets of his old air-force jacket. She gazed at him tongue-tied while shafts of excitement rippled along her nerve endings. He had the most devastating effect on all her senses she realized, as her gaze traveled over him swiftly before she spoke. He wore a crisp white shirt left open at the collar, that made a sharp contrast against his dark hair and naturally dusky skin that hinted of Celtic ancestors. His gray eyes studied her, playing havoc with her pulse rate.

"May I help you with something?" she finally asked with hesitant politeness, trying to maintain her distance. Her pulse rate seemed to be exploding under the pressure of his nearness and his silent survey of her.

"I was looking for Jim Barnes. He's not in his office," he replied with a casual indication of his dark head. This was the second time she had seen him up close, and now she noticed a small scar underneath his left eye on the crest of his high cheekbones. Had he acquired that particular souvenir in prison?

"I think he might be out in the loading bay," she said quietly.

"I've checked. And I've looked out on the airstrip. Where else could he be?" His hostile glare changed slowly to languid male scrutiny that told her she was being thoroughly and systematically examined and he didn't care too much if he were making her uncomfortable. In fact, he seemed to be enjoying it, and she sensed that he was speculating on how she rated against the other women he had known. Her face began to burn. His sharp gaze didn't miss it. And she thought she detected a flicker of some emotion in his gaze, but it was quickly hidden and the unreadable mask was back in place.

"You might try the machine shop. He sometimes stops in there to talk with Marty, the head machinist."

"Thanks." He rewarded her with one of his rare smiles.

Her gaze followed him as he disappeared into the hangar. She let out a sigh of relief. Feeling Tina's eyes on her, she looked up and then quickly bent her head. The intense annoyance on Tina's face left Laura uneasy.

That evening Laura couldn't seem to get Quint out of her mind. Home from work, she'd headed straight for her small postage-stamp-size kitchen. It was barely big enough to swing a cat in, she thought critically. Yet, a hefty portion of each weekly paycheck had to be set aside for the monthly rent for this modest apartment. But it was home and meant peace of mind, and there was no price tag one could put on that, she recalled grimly. She opened the freezer and pulled out a small casserole to put into the microwave, her thoughts on the past.

There had been a time when she would have given everything she had for this tiny apartment and for the peace and quiet it meant. It was an awful time, a time she was too ashamed to recall, a time connected with Quint. She pressed her hands to her temple as the memory hovered, a dark ominous shadow. Usually she could push it away, but tonight it insinuated itself into her conscious thought, slipping past her defenses like a silent marauder, like a thief in the night.

The knife she was using to cut up vegetables for a salad slipped out of her hand and clattered to the floor unnoticed. Visions of an empty house on a rainy Saturday afternoon focused clearly in her mind. She could see her stepfather banging around the house. He had been in one of his dark sulky moods; something had triggered it. She couldn't even remember now what it was. Neither she nor Connie, her sister, could ever figure out what started the moods off. It had never taken much, some petty misdemeanor, some imagined thing she had done wrong, something she or Connie had forgotten to buy at the supermarket. It could have been eggs stuck to the frying pan, anything. Any tiny thing was enough to set off another vicious tirade. But this day had been different.

She had been undressing in her bedroom, listening to a collection of the latest rock hits on the stereo. It had been raining all day, and she had been bored, bored, bored. As often happened, she had slipped into daydreaming, dreaming of herself as a fantastically beautiful woman, someone with feminine allure and devastating repartee, like Connie. She'd experimented with her hair, sweeping it up on her head and then turning from side to side, this way and that before the dresser mirror. Oh, how she wanted to be just like Connie. Connie was so pretty and wild and sexy, and she had tons of boyfriends.

Laura went to Connie's closet, which was bulging with clothes, and pulled out one of the latest acquisitions. It was a white crepe creation that suggested everything and revealed nothing. Laura slipped the dress off the white satin hanger. Connie was out. She'd never know. She was out getting gorgeous for one of her latest heartthrobs, someone called Quint Jones. Laura had to stop to think of his name, though only half her mind was on Connie's guy. The other half was on the alluring dress that seemed to dare her to put it on as she held it up against herself.

It was hard to keep track of all Connie's boyfriends. They never lasted long, any of them. She went through them like tissues, discarding them just as heedlessly and carelessly. None of them ever lasted as long as it took a person to get over the common cold, Laura thought as she stripped off her jeans and shirt. Standing in her lacy strapless bra and bikini briefs, she slipped the dress up over her legs, shimmying into it, and then turned with barely restrained excitement to look at herself in the floor-length mirror.

It was provocative, even on her, she'd thought as her gaze slid over her budding, willowy figure. The white dress had tantalizing cutouts that revealed glimpses of satiny skin and caressed her figure lovingly, clinging in all the right places, not missing a single curve. While she didn't quite fill the dress out the way Connie did, she was more than pleased with her blossoming femininity. She turned back toward the dresser, wanting to put the finishing touches to her exciting new image. She reached into Connie's makeup drawer, which was crammed with every beauty aid known to woman, and decided to experiment. With strokes at first awkward and hesitant, she applied liquid makeup and blusher the way she had seen Connie do it, stepping back to survey herself critically at each stage of her handiwork.

As she was outlining the upper lids of her eyes with Connie's new violet eyeliner, she could hear rumbling noises in the kitchen that made her again aware of her stepfather's presence. He was probably looking for another beer, she thought with a frown. Even over the stereo music she could hear him banging around, his temper getting more and more vicious. He always drank too much on Saturdays and got mean and aggressive. She wished he would play golf or squash and work out his frustrations that way, but he just drank and watched television and usually picked on Connie or her.

Connie was at the hairdresser's today, getting her hair highlighted. The thought suddenly eddied into her mind and cancelled out the darker reflections about her stepfather. Laura couldn't wait to see the results; whatever Connie did always seemed to turn out well. She had another date with that Quint Jones. He had lasted longer than most of Connie's boyfriends.

She picked out an eye shadow and turned back toward the mirror and, after a few deft sweeps of her finger, she noticed how miraculously her young eyes were given mysterious and sophisticated depths. Why, she looked like one of those fabulous models in the fashion magazines, she thought, amazed by her own reflection. Encouraged with the results, she applied a thick coat of mascara. It was truly amazing what makeup could do. She was transformed, utterly transformed! She had never really experimented seriously before. She struck a sultry pose and smiled, thoroughly fascinated by her own image.

With her hair swept up and makeup on, she thought she looked at least nineteen, maybe even twenty! She went to the closet to get a pair of Connie's strappy high-heeled shoes, slipped them on and walked back toward the full-length mirror with a sensuous but subtle swish of her hips, the way she had seen Connie do it countless times when she went to greet a date at the door. Why, it wasn't difficult at all. With a little practice she could be . . . sexy, too!

But her hair was wrong.

She surveyed it critically and released the pins to let it cascade down where it curled naturally to her shoulders. Usually she wore it back in a severe pony tail. This was more in keeping with her new image, more breezy and provocative. She imitated Connie's walk again and almost let·out a squeal of delight, but caught herself just in time, thinking of her stepfather in the kitchen. She raised a slender eyebrow at her image in the mirror, mocking herself and laughing softly.

She was still laughing when the bedroom door burst open. Thinking it was Connie, she whirled around, her eyes widening in dismay. Connie would throw a fit if she saw her in her best dress, the thought flashed instantly through her mind as she turned to face the doorway.

But it wasn't Connie. It was Les, her stepfather. She drew her breath in sharply as she took in the picture he made standing in the doorway, his arms braced on either side of it, giving him a hovering, aggressive air.

His voice exploded in the bedroom and the words rattled through the air like a machine gun spitting bullets.

"You stupid empty-headed little bitch. You forgot to buy me razor blades! How can I shave without razor blades? Are you just stupid, or do you like annoying me?"

She couldn't answer and stood silently staring back at him, mute with sudden fear.

"I think you do it on purpose, because you're a little scheming bitch, aren't you, just like your sister."

Les was a hulking six footer, brawny and muscular; his bulk filled the entire doorway. Once he had been good-looking, but since her mother had died, he'd gone to seed. A look of dissipation had crept in around his eyes and mouth. His shirt hung unbuttoned out of his casual slacks. The glint of a silver chain caught her eye as she stared at him, stricken with burgeoning fear as he hung poised in the doorway, as though he were going to launch an attack.

"My stupid good-for-nothing stepdaughters," he muttered beneath his breath.

Laura shrank back. He was more drunk than usual, and that meant he was more dangerous than usual.

He suddenly straightened and pushed away from the doorway as his gaze began to take in her changed appearance.

"Well…" he said suddenly. "What's this? Our shy little wallflower is starting to grow up."

He leered unsteadily at her, and she felt a new, nameless fear unwinding and growing within her. She had always been afraid of Les. His nasty turns and savage temper were something that she and Connie constantly tried to outmaneuver. They had become extremely inventive and adept at it, since life with Les was like walking on a tightrope, and one had to maintain a precarious balance at all times. Each of them protected the other. They had learned how to cajole him, jolly him along, flatter his ego, distract him. Any ploy they could possibly think of they put to full use, and they always stood together. But Connie wasn't here now.

"Oh, Connie said I could experiment with her things." It was a blatant lie, but fear spurred her on. "She's the great beauty of the family. Don't you think so, Les? She looks more like Mom every day." Laura quickly dragged her mother's memory into the conversation as a kind of protective shield, because at one time, in his own twisted way, Les had loved her mother. Why her mother had ever loved him, she wasn't at all clear about, but while her mother had been alive she had had a stabilizing effect on his mercurial temper, and he had never had the dark swings of mood he seemed to be having more and more lately.

She picked up a tissue hastily, starting to wipe away the threatening feminine allure she had so innocently projected. His narrowed eyes slid over her, and she saw something kindling in them. He stepped away from the door frame toward her.

"Connie looks more like Anne. But you have more of Anne's ways and personality. There's something about you," he murmured huskily. "Something about you that reminds me more and more of Anne. The way you move, the way you walk, the way you hold your head and the way you look at people.''

Mounting alarm grew inside Laura. ''Do you think my mother would have liked the way I'm growing up?'' she asked in a low voice, striving for some degree of normality, as the very air around them began to grow heavy with an element that was alien. Something that should not be, something that was all wrong was happening between them! Desperation began to claw at her as panic seeped into her veins.

''Yeah, I think she would like the way you're growing up,'' he said, edging even closer, ''because I like the way you're growing up, and Anne agreed with me on almost everything. She never gave me any lip, like Connie. She would agree with me that you are turning into one beautiful young woman.''

He moved across the bedroom, and Laura backed away in fright, trying not to panic. She watched in a kind of horrified, slow-motion fascination as he closed the distance. She couldn't move, but as his hand snaked out and he made a grab for her, she dodged, but not quickly enough because, suddenly, she felt herself dragged up hard against him. She gasped and began to struggle frantically, but he was too big, too strong. His hands were like a steel vise on her soft body, and his breath reeked of beer. She sobbed and pushed furiously at the hard wall of his body.

He seemed oblivious to her desperate resistance. ''You could almost take her place,'' he whispered. ''Would you like that, honey? Would you like that?''

"Stay away from me," she yelled hysterically. But his hand grabbed the hair at the back of her head and held it, held her head painfully locked, making her wince and cry out before his hot, wet mouth covered hers. Her futile protesting moans were swallowed forcefully in her throat. He molded her body into his, and she felt him pressed against her thighs, his powerful body quickening against hers. The sensation repelled and sickened her.

He thrust her backward, and she grew wild as she knew they were staggering toward the bed. She scratched and kicked and tried to jackknife her knee into his groin, but he shoved her knee down, his breathing harsh and ragged. He seized her by the back of her head again and kissed her, his tongue thrusting deep into her mouth, and she had the sensation she was gagging as she twisted and kicked wildly against him. With growing horror she felt him hard and ready against her.

"You're just like her," he said huskily. "It's been so long, so long." His grip on reality was slipping away.

Her mind, too, spiraled off, trying to project itself away from what was going to happen. She had the vague sensation of Connie's beautiful dress being torn from her body as he pushed the skirt up her thighs and lowered her onto the bed. He was above her now, on his knees, straddling her, his weight effectively pinning her down, and no matter how she twisted and turned, she couldn't move. His hands quickly undid his belt and the zipper of his pants, and slid down over her hips. She clenched her eyes shut, unable to look, and she heard her own piercing screams rend the air over and over again. He was too busy stripping off his pants to cover her mouth. Then she had heard the front door slam, and Connie burst into the room. Connie's face was white with shock and rage.

"Get away from her or, so help me, God, I'll kill you." With dazed eyes, Laura saw that Connie was shaking with anger. In her hand was a service revolver that Les kept in the front closet in case of burglars.

Les had swung around, his pants unzipped to expose white underwear, the dark look of aroused desire still in his eyes. He stood and stared at Connie for several long moments, trying to clear his head, weaving slightly from side to side. Laura remembered him running a confused hand through his hair, as if he were trying to straighten out the mess inside his head. With an air of dazed distraction he turned and looked at her lying in a crumpled heap on the bed, weeping hysterically. Whatever it was that had possessed him suddenly retreated. He swore viciously to himself and lurched from the room.

Connie stared after him. She reissued her warning in low hissing tones.

"If you ever lay so much as a finger on her, so help me, I'll get you locked up for rape or I'll kill you myself."

"How do you know it would be rape?" he sneered.

Incensed, Connie picked up the nearest thing and threw it at him. He laughed cynically and disappeared down the hallway. Connie immediately locked the door and then put down the revolver.

"My God," she whispered. "How did this happen?"

Laura could barely speak, barely get anything coherent out at all, and Connie had sat holding her, rocking her. Finally, the story of how she had been primping in front of the mirror poured out.

"Don't ever let him see you like this again! You're a budding beauty. I never complimented you or made much of it because I was afraid something like this might happen one day. I hoped you wouldn't attract his attention because you've never bothered about your looks." She got up and retrieved her handbag from the other room, then returned and sat on the bed. She pulled out a cigarette and pensively sat smoking.

Laura had lain and watched her. She had always wished she were more like Connie. Now she wished it more than ever. He would never try anything like this with Connie, she thought. Connie would kill him.

Sensing her thoughts, Connie put her arm around her.

"Don't worry. I'll always be around. You've got me. I'll never let him hurt you. I'll be more careful from now on. I'll see to it that whenever I'm out, you're baby-sitting somewhere or staying with a girl friend, and when you're home, I'll make sure I'm home. That bastard! Pretty soon I'll have a decent enough job and we'll both be out of here for good."

Laura was remembering the determined look on Connie's face when the buzzer on the microwave shattered the vivid memory. She pulled out a bubbling casserole and placed it on a mat on the snack bar and then rooted in the drawer for the silverware. With a knife, fork and spoon gripped in one hand, she took a dish from the cupboard. She put the green salad next to the turkey-and-noodle casserole. When she removed the lid, the steam rose in a mist before her eyes, and she slid onto a high stool.

Staring into space, she began to eat without tasting the dinner she had so absentmindedly prepared. The horrible memory of her stepfather invading her bedroom had faded, and another one slipped into its place. Suddenly a courtroom and a picture of herself sitting on the witness stand leaped into her mind as clearly as if it had occurred only yesterday.

She had been very young and very frightened when she had gotten up to testify that day, but there had also been the overwhelming desire to do what she had been told by those around her she *must* do. Connie had insisted that Laura lie to protect her from going to jail. And Laura had lied remarkably well.

She had pointed to the man across the crowded courtroom, looking fleetingly first at her stepfather and then back to the accused, back to Quint Jones. She knew what life without her sister around would mean; no one had to spell it out for her. She was consumed with fear at the thought of being alone with Les in that house, at the thought of Connie no longer being around to protect her. She had nowhere else to go. And Connie, the very person who had always protected her, was now demanding that she help her. She had no choice, she couldn't let Connie down; she couldn't stay alone in that house with Les. She couldn't run away. The world was a frightening place for a sixteen-year-old who didn't have the maturity to face its harsh challenges. So she lied.

''Would you please identify for the jury, the person who was behind the wheel of the car when you saw the car leave your house with your sister in it on the night of the accident?'' The prosecuting attorney had turned toward the jury, asking the question in a loud, clear voice that carried to the people in the back of the courtroom.

Laura had slowly, like an automaton, lifted her arm and pointed directly at Quinton Jones.

''He was the one,'' she had replied in a clearly audible but detached tone, her eyes looking straight through him as if he didn't exist. Then she had turned away. He had been staring at Connie, his gaze a laser of enmity beaming across the space of the courtroom. There seemed to be an unspoken message that someday the score for this unspeakable injustice would be evened between them, but Laura had turned away, thinking it would never touch her. She had not looked at him again during the entire trial. Only for that one moment. She had been asked a few more questions regarding Quint and her sister, how often he had come to the house, and then had been cross-examined by the defense.

She had held up remarkably well under the cross-examination. She had sensed the frustration of the defense counsel, who probably assumed that at sixteen she'd be very malleable, easily tripped up. He must have experienced a cold shock when she did not yield to the questions he fired at her in a continuous barrage. It was not the power of her intellect but sheer terror that had enabled her to give such a dishonest performance. First, there was her overwhelming fear of her stepfather—she knew without a doubt that she would have become his sexual outlet, and she knew without a shadow of a doubt that he would have abused her emotionally, as well. In her desperation, Connie had hammered this home to her until Laura was numb of all emotion except pure fear and the excruciating pressure of misguided loyalty toward her sister. It was those twin dark forces that had kept her so cool and collected under fire. At the time, they had not permitted any other feelings to enter into her conscious mind at all, all other emotions were instantly and remorselessly blocked. Any guilt, any compassion she felt for Quint never had a chance to even surface, so powerful were the fear and the desire to help her sister, that other feelings were banished from her mind.

When the trial was finished, Quinton Jones had gone to prison to serve time for manslaughter. She remembered seeing a small item in the local newspaper afterward, and she remembered she had felt nothing upon reading it. Absolutely nothing, just a curious detachment, almost as if she had never even been present at the trial, as if it had been someone else who had been there, not her. But she remembered the way he had looked in the courtroom, grim and silent, his dark gray eyes boring into Connie, who had betrayed him, and that was all Laura remembered. That, and a sense of relief that her sister had not been convicted.

Not long after the trial, her stepfather had had a massive stroke and died. The house was sold, and Laura and Connie lived on the money until Connie got a job. About a year after that, her sister had married a career army man. The family as Laura knew it, had evaporated into thin air. She had to fend for herself. She started a new life, changed her name and moved to another town. She went through a succession of unsatisfactory jobs until she finally found Cranston's, and an equally unsatisfactory series of furnished rooms until she at last found her tiny apartment. She had managed alone ever since.

To her amazement, she began to discover that life was not always sordid and terrifying. It was as if she had emerged from a drab chrysalis and fluttered into a golden world. But in the back of her mind something developed, too, that she had not felt before, and it was the only tarnished dark spot in her new golden world. A sense of guilt began to emerge. Her conscience, frozen by fear at the time of the trial, had begun to thaw.

Now the full awesome realization of what she had done surfaced, traveling from the preconscious level through to her conscious mind, bursting through from time to time like a dark stream. She pushed it as far back as she could, reminding herself again and again of the extenuating circumstances, but nothing could dam the dark tide of guilt that threatened to overwhelm her. She forgot that her sister was the one who had actually committed the crime, that it had been Connie who had been driving the car, that it had been Connie who had shifted Quint into the driver's seat after he had been knocked unconscious when Connie had driven the car into a tree. She'd been desperately trying to avoid hitting the drunken old man staggering across the road, but not in time. Connie never seemed to suffer any remorse before she'd conveniently disappeared.

Suddenly weary, Laura sighed. She was too tired and drained to think anymore. She couldn't undo what had been done, she told herself for the hundredth time. She recalled once again how she had looked then. It wasn't surprising that Quint hadn't recognized her. When she looked at snapshots, she hardly recognized herself at that age. She had changed so much. She had been so painfully shy that when Quint had come to the house to take her sister out, he had barely noticed her.

Was there any way she could ever make it up to him? How could anyone compensate for the years lost out of his life or the anguish of what he had been through? Her common sense told her there was no way and that she was a fool to even think there might be. But the thought kept playing over and over in her mind.

Chapter 3

You didn't forget, did you? Today's the picnic at Five Lakes Park." Tina's voice percolated over the telephone wire with energy and enthusiasm.

"Say you'll come along," she begged.

Laura hadn't dressed yet and was still wearing a white terry-cloth robe, belted at the waist, her bare legs and feet exposed by its brief hem. Her gaze traveled toward the window. It was a beautiful day, and she really didn't have anything much to do.

"Come on," Tina urged. "It was fantastic last year. Everybody was there. The food was great, and they had live entertainment in the evening, a really terrific country-and-western group, and sports and canoeing during the day. It didn't finish until nearly midnight. You would be foolish to miss it, since nothing much ever happens in this town."

Tina's enthusiasm was infectious. Laura felt excited by the prospect of going to a picnic. She hadn't been to anything remotely like one since she was a small child, before her father had died and her stepfather had come into her life. Those times had been among the happiest of all her memories. A desire to recapture some of that youthful joy surged inside her. It was the deciding factor, that, and the fact that Tina was inevitably good company.

When they reached the park, the afternoon seemed to explode with children shrieking and shouting as they burned off excess energy, running in and out of the picnic tables and around the adjoining areas while the more sedate grown-ups nearby engaged in quieter conversation and music drifted over everything from the nearby pavilion. All Laura's senses were filled up by the beauty of the golden, languid afternoon and the swaying dappled shade of the willow trees that enveloped the people sitting beneath them. She felt suddenly charged with new energy and the heady joie de vivre that comes at such moments. She gazed slowly around the picnic area, glad she had come.

"See what I mean," Tina announced gaily. "The world and his wife are here. Let's hope there are a few spare men floating around somewhere, too," she added dryly. "I know there's a crowd here from Cranston's because at least a half dozen people told me they were coming."

Laura scanned the faces at the picnic tables. The leafy bows of the trees shaded the people spread out beneath them in a human melange. Mothers hugging young babies, husbands sitting nearby, grandparents reclining in gaily colored lawn chairs. Across the adjoining lawns and playing fields, impromptu games of softball and volleyball had sprung up. In the distance were the shining waters of the Five Lakes, man-made lakes joined together by a series of canals and dotted with canoeists.

As Laura and Tina edged their way along, weaving through the crowds and the tables of the picnicking area, several colleagues from Cranston Aviation waved to them and shouted. They waved back eagerly and walked over to join them.

"Come and sit down with us. Have you eaten yet?" Mary McGovern, one of the bookkeepers, pointed to the food stands that lined the picnic area.

"There's chili and fresh ears of corn, hamburgers, hot dogs, potato salad, coleslaw. You name it, they've got it. And the tab is being picked up by local businesses. Everybody's been stuffing themselves. I'm so glad you both came. Sit down and chat awhile," she added, pointing to an empty seat beside her and another on the bench diagonally across from her. Warmed by her friendliness, Laura and Tina sat down.

"Have you been here long?" Laura asked.

"Since about ten o'clock. I come every year, and I wouldn't miss it for the world. The annual picnic is the social highlight of the year for a small town like Waverly. You've never been before, have you?" She directed her question at Laura as she plastered a hot dog with mustard and relish.

"No, I've only worked at Cranston's for about a year, and when I came last summer the picnic was already over and done with. But I've heard people talk about it from time to time in the canteen."

"Well, once you've been to one, I doubt whether you'll ever miss another one. It's a wonderful day out for the entire family. There's something for everybody."

"Are there many people here from Cranston's?" Laura asked. She scanned the picnic area, not able to think of anything else to say for the moment and wanting to avoid an embarrassing lull in the conversation.

"Nearly the whole clerical department is here. Jim and his wife and his daughters are here with their families. Then I saw one or two of the mechanics and their families and some of the pilots. They were all playing softball over there. That new pilot Jim hired was playing, too. He's awfully good-looking. I don't know his name. Keeps to himself, doesn't he? I think they're still playing, as a matter of fact, if you want to go and watch them," Mary said, turning and shading her eyes with her hand as she gazed toward the playing field.

Tina leaned forward immediately. "Did you hear that!" she whispered excitedly as Mary excused herself and went to talk to a woman who was waving to her from several picnic tables down.

"Yes, I heard. I thought you crossed him off your list," Laura reminded her with a hint of edginess creeping into her voice. "You said he wasn't interested."

"I'm going to have one more try. Persistence pays off," Tina added resolutely.

"Not in everything," Laura said.

Tina was oblivious to her comment. "Come on. Let's go and watch the softball game."

"You go. I'll stay here," Laura said, hanging back. The last thing she wanted to do was to attract the attention of Quint Jones again.

"Come with me. Please," Tina begged. "You've got your mystery man. Give me a chance. I need some moral support."

What could she do? Laura didn't think Tina needed any kind of support; she seemed to be more in need of restraint. But Laura didn't want to arouse Tina's suspicions or get her angry, so she rose warily and walked alongside her, wishing fervently she hadn't come to the picnic at all.

As she walked, she tried to think of some way out of this rapidly unfolding situation that was fraught with all kinds of alarming possibilities.

"Look, the game is breaking up. They're finished, there's nothing much to watch," Laura remarked with relief, catching hold of Tina's arm and gently trying to pull her back in the direction of the picnic tables.

"Oh, yes, there is," Tina whispered victoriously. "There he is. Let's go say hello."

"You go say hello. I'm going back to get something to eat. I'm feeling pretty ravenous."

"Don't go. I need you with me!" Tina smiled at the group of players heading off the field toward the drink stand nearby. "I think I'll have a cool drink. How about you?" she asked in a clearly audible voice for the benefit of those approaching.

With a little sigh of resignation, Laura swung back around and immediately saw him. He was taller than the other men, so he stood out. Without his usual flying jacket, his leanly muscled frame was exposed. He had on a navy T-shirt, which showed well-developed shoulders and arms and a broad chest tapering to a flat belly, and faded jeans, which clung to his long legs and rode low on his hips.

As he walked across the field with the other pilots and mechanics, his head turned slowly toward her, singling her out of the crowd as if drawn by some invisible radar. A strong, undeniable current shot through her. Had he recognized her? As the men moved closer, his gaze pinned and held her with its slow, sweeping and very male appraisal. She had worn a white dress with a long full skirt and a fitted bodice with a halter neck that outlined her full breasts. Again, he made no effort to conceal his all-too-clear interest. She flushed under his lingering inspection. She tried to hang back and impulsively started to turn away, almost without realizing what she was doing.

Tina sensed it, and her hand clamped on Laura's arm. She hissed in her ear through clenched teeth. "Don't you dare leave me here on my own, or I'll strangle you with my bare hands."

"I wasn't going anywhere," Laura said, feeling a tremor run through her.

The mechanics and pilots recognized Tina and Laura from the offices at Cranston's. "Do you two want to have a go?" one said holding up the bat.

"No, thanks," Tina warbled.

"How about a canoe race?" another suggested with a gleam in his eye. Tina shook her head again as Laura stood silently watching.

"The last time I went out in a canoe, my date didn't speak to me for a week. Because we went round and round in circles."

The men laughed.

"Oh, there's a knack to it," another offered.

"Yes, but I never discovered what it was."

"Come on, we'll show you."

In spite of her discomfort, Laura began to smile at the good-natured verbal jousting going on as Tina resolutely declined their invitations. Everyone seemed to be talking at once, going into the mysteries of paddling a canoe. Laura looked up and found Quint's gray eyes studying her silently.

The smile faded from her face. My God, she thought in quiet desperation, he was singling her out. It was no longer fear of recognition that surged through her, it was something else infinitely more potent. The lighthearted banter over canoeing faded into the background as she took in every detail; his dark hair ruffled by the May breeze, the fine sheen of perspiration on his forehead, the navy T-shirt clinging to his broad shoulders and his lean, hard torso. She tore her gaze away breathlessly just as one of the men yelled, "Why don't we cool off and go for a swim instead!"

Laura felt instantly relieved, as if the man had come to her rescue. There were shouts of agreement to hurry it up because it was only a short time before the sun set. They hastily finished their drinks. Then all of them, including Quint, disappeared down the pathway leading to the changing rooms. Tina and Laura watched them go.

"He really is a closed book, that's all I can say," Tina commented. "He never says more than two words at a time, and he doesn't say *that* much if he can get away with it."

Laura, still wrapped in the effects of Quint's silent perusal, thought shakily that he didn't have to say anything.

"Have you finally given up on him?" she asked.

"Yes, I concede defeat. It's impossible to get to know that one. Oh, well, there are other fish in the sea," Tina added, bouncing back with characteristic optimism. Nothing kept Tina down for long, it was one of the most attractive sides of her personality and one of the things Laura liked about her most.

They stood for a while, sipping cool drinks, watching the musicians under the pavilion getting ready to play. Laura stood wrestling with the strange sensations Quint had stirred up inside her.

"Let's stay here for a while," Tina suggested. "The music will be starting soon. They're putting on a group straight out of Nashville, one with a hit high on the charts."

"We haven't had anything to eat yet," Laura said, stalling. "We can come back here when the music begins." Her gaze swept the water where she could hear the distant shouts of voices. She turned away, relieved to be distanced from those enigmatic gray eyes.

The sun sank into the waters, and the golden glow faded, giving way to lantern light in the picnic area and pavilion. With Tina growing increasingly restless at her side, Laura ate slowly and dragged out the meal for as long as she possibly could. She knew that the men would have finished with their swim and changed, and she wanted to avoid meeting Quint again.

The melodic, easy rhythms of country-and-western music floated across the whole park, instantly saturating the atmosphere with a mellow mood. People began to drift toward the pavilion.

Tina urged Laura along. "We'll never meet anyone sitting over here. Come on."

Reluctantly, Laura followed.

When they reached the edge of the now-crowded pavilion, a young man from the accounts department at Cranston's immediately engaged Tina in conversation. Laura stood listening to the music.

"Do you like country-and-western?"

Startled, she swung around and found herself face-to-face with Quint again. He had changed after swimming into a white shirt, left open at the collar and with the sleeves rolled up. Dark pants outlined his long legs and narrow hips. Her gaze swept over his powerful physique and stunning masculinity. She swiftly reprimanded herself silently, telling herself that she had to stop reacting so visibly every time he came near. But it was too late. She could see the expression in his eyes grow wintry and the skin across his high cheekbones grow taut. It was clear that her edginess irritated him. He continued to study her with something in his eyes that was close to amusement mingled with scorn.

"Tell me something," he said evenly. "Does the entire human race scare the hell out of you, or is it just me? I don't remember ever having this effect on a woman before. I used to think some women found me attractive. But maybe I was getting too bigheaded. Well, there's no chance of that when I'm around you," he went on, as Laura stared back at him dumbstruck. "Because when I'm around you, I get the feeling that I look like Cyclops, or maybe Quasimodo on a bad day.'' His mouth quirked into a rusty smile, but there was an undercurrent of bitterness eddying beneath his words, mixed with a teasing sensuality that seemed to come easily to him.

Laughter burst from her. It came partly from the expulsion of tension and partly from the humor in what he said. A man with a sense of humor always turned her on, and she responded easily, almost without thinking.

''I know for a fact that women find you attractive,'' she said immediately, thinking of Tina, not to mention herself. ''And you're quite good-looking. You don't remind me at all of Quasimodo.'' She paused for effect. ''He was short you know.'' She laughed softly, trying to cover up the anxiety that was building inside her underneath the surveillance of those silent gray marauding eyes.

''Was he?'' Quint retorted dryly as his gaze slid from her head and lingered on the plunging halter neckline then slipped down to her legs and back up again.

He was angry, she could see that, but he was also interested. Very interested from the look in his eyes.

''You still haven't told me why you nearly jump out of your skin whenever I'm around.''

And he was also not easily deterred, she quickly noted. But then she wouldn't have expected anything less from him. She tried tossing away his observations as if they were completely unfounded.

''You must be imagining things. I don't jump,'' she murmured softly.

He didn't say anything for a long moment, his silvery gaze turning opaque. When he did speak, he gave added emphasis to his words, saying them slowly, the look in his eyes underscoring his meaning, so that there would be no missing his intent.

"I may imagine things about you, but that's not one of them," he said quietly with the same searing sensuality she had seen glimpses of before. His words sent a current flashing through her.

He continued to watch her closely before he continued.

"You jump like a scared rabbit whenever I'm around, and I want to know why." The wary almost hostile look returned. The clean-cut lines and planes of his angular face were partly in shadow and partly illuminated by the lantern swinging overhead in the evening breeze making him seem more dangerous than usual.

"That's not true," she said defensively, leaning back against the post that supported the roof of the pavilion, trying to strike a casual pose under his probing gaze.

His eyes narrowed at her continuous denial of the obvious. He wasn't going to be deterred. He slid one arm up and rested it on the overhang with deceptive nonchalance, so that he was peering down at her as she stood with her back against the post.

"I really don't know what you're talking about," she reaffirmed brazenly, still persisting in her lie as she experienced the sensation of his lean rangy masculinity pinning her to the post and holding her captive. The skin grew taut over his handsome features, and the small triangular scar on the crest of his cheek grew more noticeable.

"Liar," he accused softly. "We both know you do, and we both know why," he said with an accompanying ruthless twist to his mouth.

His words made her begin to shake, as she thought he had finally recognized her. She stood mutely gazing up at him, not daring to speak or move at all, suddenly feeling light-headed and dizzy.

They were standing at the edge of the pavilion off to one side. The music in the background kept their voices from carrying so that no one could hear them. But they could hear each other plainly enough.

"You know about me, don't you?" he demanded in a voice that was like Antarctic ice as he overshadowed her.

She relaxed visibly. He hadn't recognized her. She breathed in deeply and shakily with relief. The clean scent of him eddied around her, filling her senses. She suddenly felt drugged by his nearness, and her whole body seemed to be rendered boneless by it. She experienced the strange sensation that if he reached out for her at that precise moment, he could have had her. The thought almost unnerved her completely. To offset the potent effect he had on her, she persisted in her denial, hoping to bluff her way out of the increasingly fraught situation. It was as if he had a net around her and was slowly drawing it in tighter and tighter, so she pretended complete ignorance.

"Know what about you?" She laughed softly. "I don't know anything about you," she added on another shaky note, and started to shift away from the post, wanting only to escape from his burning inquisition. His other hand came down like a guillotine blade on the other side of the post, cutting off her escape route, trapping her.

"You know about me. Don't you. *Don't lie,*" he said in a deadly soft tone.

The words "don't lie" had a telling effect on her. She had lied once where he was concerned. And the results had been catastrophic. She wouldn't lie again. She lowered her eyes, partly because of the effect his nearness was having on her and partly from remorse, then she looked up at him through a screen of dark lashes.

"Yes. I know," she finally admitted quietly.

His silver gaze raked her. His hands reached out and closed around her upper arms, and he dragged her away from the post, as if he despised this nonchalant deception she had been perpetrating and as if he wanted to emphasize what he was going to say next and to make sure she listened to every syllable. He grabbed her wrist and pulled her from the pavilion. His voice was low-pitched, but strong emotion poured into every word as he spoke, so that his words vibrated through her entire being as he ground them out. She fixed her eyes on the rigid planes of his face.

"I want you to know that what *I've got* is not catching. I'm friendly and peace loving when I'm not abused. I even had a mother and father who found me lovable. I do not carry a deadly weapon around with me. I would also like to add that apart from that one black period in my life, I was never in trouble with the law or anyone else for that matter." His gray eyes bit into her, and Laura gazed back at him transfixed, feeling as though she were being buffeted by a violent storm and that she was sinking under his spell as he went on.

"But I don't expect you to believe that, because nobody ever does."

But she did believe him. She knew that what he was saying was perfectly true.

"I believe you. I know you're not dangerous," she said, gazing steadily back at him, mesmerized by the strange undercurrents that seemed to be racing between them. Her words had the ring of truth, and she saw the expression in his eyes flicker fleetingly in disbelief. That wasn't the reaction he was used to getting from someone who knew about him, she thought, and she decided to capitalize on it.

"I just like to keep myself to myself. Like you do," she retorted airily. Even to her own ears, it sounded like a lame excuse, but she hurried on, intent on taking advantage of the slight edge she had gained in this strange duel of words and emotions that raced between them. "That's why it may *seem* to you that I'm avoiding you, but I'm not," she added with unconvincing assurance. His eyes bored straight through her, and the corner of his mouth developed a cynical twist. Her attempts at playacting disintegrated completely. Why did he have to be so— His voice snapped like a whip interrupting her thoughts.

"Try again. I'm not convinced," he stated in that hard, flat tone she was coming to know. All his defenses were up, and wariness swirled around him like an invisible cloak.

She drew in another shaky breath. "It's the truth," she blurted, without thinking of the consequences.

"Prove it to me," he challenged quietly, holding her gaze locked into his.

"How?" She stared blankly at him, completely taken aback.

"Let me take you out to dinner."

It was clear he was testing her. Laura's lovely green eyes widened in surprise. And again she saw the cynical look invade his now-leaden gray eyes.

"You just gave me your answer. The truth is written all over your face." There was a note of resignation in his voice that tore at something soft and vulnerable inside her. "I would appreciate it, though, if you wouldn't go around telling everyone what you know about me," he added coldly.

Laura could see all the shutters closing around him as he distanced himself from her. The emotion he had displayed was quickly withdrawn as his face became impassive.

"But that's probably asking too much of a woman."

It was his heart-wrenching cynicism and the parting shot that it would be expecting too much of a woman that did it.

"I...will go out with you," Laura heard herself say. The words shot out of her mouth, springing from a deep well of guilt and an overriding desire to somehow make up for what she had done, what two women had done to him.

He stared at her silently for a long suspended moment, then released her arm.

"When?" he asked. The question was a swift sharp demand.

"When would you like?" she asked, thinking he would say next weekend.

"Tomorrow evening," he fired back, and this time she managed to suppress her surprise. Another wry smile tugged at the corner of his mouth. He had called her bluff.

She wanted to dispel that look in his eyes. "You have my word. I want to put your mind at rest." She said the words almost defiantly, gazing at him unwaveringly. "I haven't told anyone about you. Nor do I intend to tell anyone." He considered her words as though he neither believed nor disbelieved her, but would adopt a wait-and-see policy.

"Where do you live," he asked. "Or would you rather meet me somewhere, so I don't find out?" he challenged.

Laura gave him instructions on how to find her apartment, and then he asked her where she would like to go.

"You decide," she answered with a husky tremor in her voice, suddenly realizing, to her own shattered amazement, what she had done.

"I'll pick you up tomorrow evening at eight." A smile flickered. He seemed like a cat who had just caught himself a juicy little mouse. "I've got to leave now. I'm taking one of the mechanics home."

"I'll see you, then," she replied offhandedly, still striving to convey a casual air.

He didn't look convinced, and that same smile again curved the corners of his mouth as he pushed away from the overhang and walked off. Her gaze followed him, and she breathed an audible sigh. Good grief. What had she done? She couldn't believe she had actually made a date with the man she had been bent on avoiding. Why? The question loomed in her mind like an accusation. Because she wanted to make up to him somehow for what she had done, she conceded slowly, because she felt guilty and couldn't stand to see that look of hardened cynicism in his eyes. That look that said he expected nothing but abuse from people. That look that she felt partly responsible for putting there. That was the reason why, she told herself quietly.

But was it the only reason? she wondered.

Chapter 4

The following evening as she got ready for her date with Quint, Laura was distracted, her mind churning with misgivings. Had she been crazy to let him come here? She would let him take her out this once. That was all. It would prove to him that she wasn't avoiding him because of what she knew about him. He would see that people would give him a second chance, she told herself, as she kept one eye on the clock. But she didn't face up to the other feelings that were causing havoc within her. The way he made her feel, the fact that she found herself wanting to go out with him, the sheer excitement that rippled through her entire being. No, she convinced herself that it was just this one time that she would go out with him. It was for his benefit that she was doing this. Satisfied with her conclusions, she surveyed her appearance critically.

She had chosen a two-piece outfit. A fitted jacket in soft white wool and a slim black skirt. The jacket could be removed if it was hot in the restaurant. Underneath she wore a white satin camisole held up by narrow straps. She slipped on black patent-leather pumps, balancing on first one leg and then the other while one hand rested on the dresser top. She straightened and smoothed the skirt and jacket, and then picked up a brush and ran it through her hair, which cascaded in curls to her shoulders. As she clipped gold rings into her ears, she wondered if she should wear her hair up or down.

She leaned forward, peering into the dresser mirror and put the finishing touches to her makeup. She was still debating about her hair when the door buzzer interrupted the silence. Picking up her handbag, she went to answer the door.

A strange broad-shouldered man in an expensive-looking deep blue business suit, light blue shirt and deep red-and-blue-striped tie stood gazing at her. After a double take, she realized it was Quint, transformed by his clothes and looking breathtakingly handsome. He seemed on edge and wary, as if he thought she might disappear at any moment in a wisp of smoke. His whole manner was pervaded by it, as if he expected to be turned down at the last minute, and he had put on that veneer of hardness that protected him from the abuse he expected from anyone who knew about him. It wrenched something deep inside Laura, and whatever misgivings she'd had about letting him come to pick her up at her home and take her out were erased.

"I thought you might have changed your mind." A soft challenge flickered in the expression of his hard, good-looking face and adamant eyes.

Who could blame him, she thought. He had every reason to think that way.

"No, you're stuck with me. I haven't changed my mind." She laughed softly, deftly turning the tables.

A seldom used smile caught at his mouth, and they left the apartment and walked out into the balmy night air to his car. It was one of the latest models, and she wondered how he had managed it. It couldn't be easy to get credit to finance a car when you had a criminal record. He must have noticed her assessing gaze, because as he opened the door to the Jaguar, he enlightened her.

"If you're wondering how I managed to get a new car, I want to reassure you that I didn't steal it. While I was serving time, a relative died and left me the bulk of her estate. She was the only person who believed in me," he added grimly. "She knew that all my savings went on expenses for the trial." He seemed locked into a deep submerged anger.

"But money can never compensate for the years stolen out of my life or the respect that I lost. Or the struggle I had trying to make my way back into the world once I was released," he added, unable to disguise the bitter edge to his words. "I wasn't guilty, you know. I was convicted of manslaughter—but I wasn't the one driving the car!"

She turned away, her eyes suddenly haunted, not wanting him to see her expression, and she slid into the front seat. He slammed the car door and looked at her for a long moment before he walked around to the other side of the car.

They dined at an exclusive out-of-the-way restaurant that served New Orleans-style food and featured sultry jazz music. And though they talked of many things, the conversation kept veering dangerously back to his imprisonment, as if it had some strange, fascinating magnetic pull that couldn't be avoided, as if it demanded to be discussed and gotten out of the way or else it would only cast a pall over everything.

"What made you come to Cranston's for a job?" she asked, wondering about the ease with which fate had thrown them together again. She had forgotten that at the time of the trial he had only recently left the air force. It must have been mentioned during the trial, but it had slipped her mind entirely. If she had remembered she would never have taken the job with an air-freight company like Cranston's, she reflected regretfully. It was too late for the wisdom of hindsight now.

"I had a hard time finding a job at first when I got out," he said, signaling a wine steward. He came and took their order and quickly disappeared.

"I had a succession of jobs before I came here, but they were only to fill up my time. I always wanted to get back into commercial flying. But with my record I couldn't make the major airlines. And then I saw this job advertised. Jim seemed desperate for a pilot. That's why he hired me," Quint added sardonically.

"He also thought you were a good man," she interceded quickly, meeting his gaze steadily. She saw something flicker in his eyes again. Which was just as quickly hidden. She decided to change the subject.

They talked at length about Cranston's and how it had grown over the years and about Jim Barnes and some of the other employees.

"What do you think of the men you work with? The mechanics you were playing baseball with at the park? They look like a lot of fun."

"They're a great bunch of guys."

"They seem to like you."

"They don't know about me," he asserted flatly as his expression hardened and his eyes became wintry.

Laura's slender fingers slid up and down the fragile stem of the wineglass. They couldn't seem to get away from his time spent in prison, she thought. The conversation veered back to it like a boomerang. She looked at him helplessly for a long moment, pleading with her eyes, not knowing what to say, thinking it was better to say nothing and let him direct the conversation. She didn't seem to be doing a very good job of it. His expression softened. And the creases around his mouth deepened as he treated her to another one of his rusty smiles. Everything inside her seemed to melt.

"I'm sorry. I've developed a natural wariness, a suspicion of everyone and everything, especially when I'm around a woman. It was a woman who..." He apparently decided it wasn't worth going into. "I can't always control it. Maybe in time it will fade." He glanced over his shoulder, ostensibly to look for the waiter, but in reality to avoid her eyes.

"Do you hate all women?" she ventured quietly as a sense of guilt shot through her.

"Do I hate them? No." He laughed softly, a smile curving the corner of his mouth. "Would I be here now with you if I did? I'm not immune to women and their...obvious attraction, especially yours," he said, letting his gaze slide over her in a sizzling, lingering path. A heavy sensuality surfaced between them. "But I don't trust them an inch," he added.

A chill ran through Laura at his words.

There was a group of musicians playing some slow jazz. He glanced over at them and back at her.

"Would you like to dance?" he asked as he rose slowly from the chair. His gray eyes spoke a silent message. It was clear he was trying to make amends and smooth over their awkward attempts at conversation.

"Yes," she said. Anything would be better than this, she thought.

They walked out onto the small, crowded dance floor, disappearing into the crush of people. Laura looked up at him as his arms slid around her and he pulled her toward him. Her arm slid over his shoulder until her hand curved around his neck and seemed to rest there as if it belonged, brushing against the dark hair above his collar. It was luxurious and thick, and her fingers sank into it.

They stared at each other without moving for a long moment. His gray eyes probed hers with crushing impact and a compelling need that required no translation. She felt a white-hot, devastating reaction to it and suddenly wondered what it would be like to have him make love to her. With searing certainty she knew that he knew exactly what she was thinking and that he was thinking exactly the same thing. What was even more devastating was that he didn't care if she knew. The look in his eyes told her that he was past caring what people thought.

"I don't believe I've told you that I think you're the most beautiful woman I've met, before or since I got out. And I hope you can't read my mind, because you're going to be embarrassed if you can." He laughed softly and drew her closer.

Then they danced through two languid blues numbers, not saying anything, locked into each other's arms and surrounded by the press of couples dancing around them. He held her tightly and pressed his face against her temple. A tremor ran through his powerful frame, as if some long repressed surge of pent-up desire was suddenly released within him.

"You feel so damned good," he murmured hoarsely into her ear. "Do you know that?" His low-pitched voice and the raw emotion in it assaulted all her senses, triggering a powerful surge of desire deep within her. She wanted to melt into him, to fill every nook and cranny of his body with her own soft curves. He sensed it immediately, and with an aching need, his hand slid to the lowest part of her back to press her into him.

"Do you know how many nights I lay awake in prison dreaming of holding a woman in my arms again? Someone just like you. When I got out, I thought no one like you would ever..."

His words sent searing guilt through her. A woman like her! She stiffened in his arms and pulled back. Enigmatic gray eyes searched her face, puzzled by the change.

"You don't know anything about me," she warned with a low, husky tremor in her voice and a baleful expression in her eyes. "I...could have done something...terrible."

He grinned disbelievingly down at her. They stood almost still, barely moving at all.

"I'll bet you've never even had a parking ticket." He paused and then spoke slowly, watching her face closely for her reaction, his voice dropping softly and intimately. "I'd also bet there have been few men in your bed."

His words had an immediate dizzying effect, followed by a rush of something so inexplicable coursing through her that it unnerved her completely and left her feeling vulnerable, as if she suddenly found herself without clothes in a room full of people. Other couples were moving around them. Quint and Laura were both oblivious to everything and anyone but each other.

"You shouldn't talk to me like this," she murmured.

"Shouldn't I?" he replied, looking completely unrepentant as his marauding gray eyes slid over her face.

With a bewildered distraction, Laura wondered, Why me? He could have had any number of women at Cranston's or anywhere else for that matter. Why her.

Gazing back at him steadily, she blurted out her thoughts. "Why haven't you gotten yourself a woman? Why didn't you find yourself a woman, any woman, when you came out?" she asked almost with a note of exasperation in her voice.

"It's not the same," he growled, drawing her closely into his arms again and nuzzling the side of her face. "I didn't want just any woman. It's just going through the motions, with someone who doesn't turn you on.

By now you must realize the effect you have on me." His hand slipped down her back to press her into him again, and she felt as though she were being sucked down into some deep dark abyss. "If you let me, I'll show you that I'm not half as dangerous as I look. And maybe in time you won't jump out of your skin when I come near you."

She had the crazy desire to slip her hands inside his jacket to feel the hardness of his back under her hands and to move closer to him. She thought she must be losing her mind, and she rested her head against his neck, closing her eyes as a languid torpor spread through her. His hand moved compulsively over her hip, making desire eddy deep within her. She heard him groan softly, and he suddenly molded her to him as if he could never get enough of her.

Neither one of them said anything. It was all too clear what was happening. She was intoxicated, she dimly realized. Everything about him was intoxicating. She breathed his scent deeply as her face brushed the side of his neck just below his ear. Suddenly the music stopped and the band took a break. Quint and Laura stepped back, Laura slightly dazed.

Her face was flushed, and she knew it was not from the heat of the dance floor but from a heat that was generated between the two of them. They moved back to the table, and she felt herself burning after the way she had responded to him. The look in Quint's eyes told her that he had felt her unequivocal response in his arms, that he hadn't missed the flush on her face and the languor in her eyes that testified to her swift arousal.

They both knew how things stood between them. The conversation was only superficial, while underneath swift strong currents passed between them. The irony was too much. Laura wanted to laugh hysterically. Here she was with the very man she had planned to avoid at all costs. The man she had planned to keep a low profile around, who hopefully would find her indistinguishable from the furniture. And he had separated her from all that, singled her out, chosen her from everybody else, and now, irony of ironies, she found herself on a date with him and, to her stunned amazement, found herself strongly attracted to him both emotionally and physically.

The waiter appeared with their food, and they began to eat, talking of inconsequential things, deliberately avoiding the thorny subject of his past imprisonment. She learned about his youth, about where he had grown up, where he had gone to school and that he had always dreamed of flying. Then he told her about how he had gone into the air force and trained as an officer and a fighter pilot and why he had decided he didn't want to spend a lifetime there. She told him a bit about herself, that her parents had both died when she was young, which was partially true. Her father had died when she was young, but her mother had married again and had not died until several years later. She told him that she had been raised in a nearby town, giving an aunt's address as the place where she'd grown up. He seemed satisfied with that, though she noticed he watched her speculatively and didn't say much.

At the back of her mind she suddenly began to wonder what he would do if he found out who she really was. For some reason up until now she had only been obsessed with wondering if he would recognize her. She hadn't given much thought to what he would actually *do* if he discovered who she was. Now it suddenly struck her like summer lightening. Would he try to even the score, try to extract some kind of revenge?

They went to see a film after dinner. In the theater she found she was very much aware of him next to her. She had difficulty concentrating on the film, in fact, because of this strange heightened awareness she felt near him. When he stretched out his long legs, his leanly muscled thigh and knee lightly grazed her own and she felt heat rush in her body, and she was glad of the darkened theater. His hand slid to hers and covered it, a simple gesture, but with him it seemed highly erotic.

The voice of common sense kept pounding in her head, warning her off. No, no, it can't be. You've got to stop this. You can't let this happen. You mustn't see him again. When the evening is over, thank him politely and then never see him again. You are a fool if you don't, an absolute fool.

His hand tightened around hers, and he placed it on his knee.

She concentrated on the film. The love scenes only heightened the sensations that were running in strong currents between them. She felt as though she had a bad case of sunburn on her face. In fact, her whole body seemed to be on fire. She was relieved at last when the film came to an end and the house lights went on. They rose and moved through the crowd. She felt his hand rest possessively on her waist as they walked out into the balmy summer evening. The evening breeze felt good on her skin.

On the way home in the car, he stopped at a traffic light and turned to look at her. His gray-eyed gaze, which lingered lazily on her face, made her flesh quiver as if it had been pierced by hundreds of quick sensuous darts.

"Will you let me take you out again?"

She drew a long, deep, ragged breath and stared out the window trying to stop the rush of emotions he triggered inside her.

"I don't know," she said evasively. Use your head, her common sense ordered sternly.

"What do you mean, you don't know?" The cynicism that had been absent from his voice for most of the evening was now trickling back. His face became cold and impassive.

"I think it would be better for both of us if we didn't . . . see one another again."

"Why?" The question was flat and terse. Her gaze swung to meet his. No attempt was made to disguise or soften the silent growing anger that accompanied the tautness of the lines of his face.

"Because we both work in the same place. That's always tricky."

"Is that the real reason?"

"Yes," she whispered.

"Liar." He laughed derisively.

There was a sizzling silence. He drove at a fast clip then, ignoring her and concentrating on the road. She knew that she had angered him deeply. And she wanted to say yes and yield to her own desire. But the sensible part of her cried out silently that to do so was playing with fire. She wished fervently that all of her could be wise and sensible. Her heart didn't feel wise, her body didn't feel wise. She responded to him like she had no other man she had ever met before and *that* certainly wasn't wise.

The car lurched to a stop in front of her apartment.

"You don't have to see me to the door," she said quietly, thinking that he would want to get away from her as fast as humanly possible, but she was mistaken.

"I want to," he replied in that low-pitched, determined way that left no room for argument.

Without another word he slid out of the car, slammed the door hard behind him and walked around to her side. Avoiding his eyes she got out, and they walked toward the apartment door. It was shadowed by a large tree and shrubs, secluded from the street. As soon as they were there, she reached into her handbag for the key and started to murmur her thanks.

Strong hands gripped her arms, turning her around, and she saw a quick flash of intent gray eyes before his mouth found hers with unerring accuracy. He trapped her against the doorway with long, drugging, hypnotic kisses. His mouth was tentative at first, coaxing a response. Then he broke off, and his mouth touched her cheekbones, the curve of her neck and then her lips again, leaving a trail of desire slowly unwinding deep within her. She tried pushing him away.

"Please stop," she whispered huskily as she struggled in his arms.

"I've been aching for this all night, and so have you. Don't tell me to stop, Laura." The look in his silvery-gray eyes dared her to refute what he said. Then he lowered his head and kissed her with a burning, tormented hunger, as if she were compensation for all the deprivation he had endured. He pressed his lean, hard ranginess into her, so that she could feel the sharp point of his hipbones, the long line of his thighs, the hard wall of his chest. Her hands clenched on his shoulders, then slid to the back of his neck when his mouth parted hers. His tongue mated with hers with a hungry insistence until he broke off the kiss again.

"Let me touch you," he whispered raggedly against the side of her face. "I want so much to touch you."

His plea, which held a note of longing, as if it were something he had dreamed of for an interminably long time, held her mesmerized and receptive. Her own senses were reeling, and she made no protest as his hand undid the buttons on her jacket and then slipped inside over the satin camisole. She wore no bra, and she heard the swift sharp intake of his breath. Then his mouth closed over hers again, and his large hand gently crushed one full breast. He groaned softly, deep in his throat, and his large frame shuddered. Laura felt her legs turning to jelly as the growing urgency of his blind caresses aroused her like the strongest aphrodisiac. He lowered his head again and kissed her deeply this time, and his hands slid underneath the camisole, exploring more boldly.

The touch of his hand on the bare skin of her breasts sent streamers of desire between her legs as his rough thumbs caressed the soft nipples, arousing them into excruciatingly tender sensitive points. Then he pressed his rapidly hardening body against hers, whispering her name into the curve of her neck and telling her in no uncertain terms with the silent language of his body what he wanted. She moaned softly in response. She had never been aroused so quickly and so intensely in her entire life. Everything was fading around her except this swift, urgent desire that he was filling her with. The kiss deepened now, and their tongues touched wildly. Eventually his hand slid to the lower part of her back, molding her intimately to him, and she felt the full power of him, his full arousal. It took her breath away and filled her with an intense desire to have him deep inside her. Her arms tightened, and her fingers sank into the thick hair at the back of his neck as she kissed him back wildly so that they were locked into an embrace in which it was impossible to tell where she began and he left off.

He grimaced with need, sucking in his breath harshly, one hand sliding underneath her skirt and grasping her hips. Then something, some iron control, some sense of propriety, brought him back to his senses, and he hastily pulled her skirt back down and shoved himself away from her.

Just as suddenly as he had initiated the passionate embrace, he broke it off. He was shaking perceptibly with the effort it was costing him. His breathing was noticeably disturbed, and raw desire was glazing his eyes so strongly that it was as if he had just been awoken from a deep sleep.

Laura leaned her head against the apartment door. She closed her eyes, not daring to look at him another second, knowing that she would be sucked back down into that quicksand of desire, struggling to regain some shred of composure and to rise above it.

"I want to see you again." He laughed softly. "That's pretty obvious. You asked if I hated all women. Well, I certainly don't hate you." His voice had deepened, made rough with aroused desire.

"I'll have to think about it," she murmured shakily. Her whole body seemed to still be pulsating from the rush of desire that had sprung up between them. He knew from the way she had responded that she was strongly attracted to him, she thought miserably. It was impossible to hide. There was no use denying it. Inexperienced though she was, she realized what was happening to them. She had known all along that she was attracted to him, but she had never dreamed how powerful that attraction could be.

"What's there to think about? You don't like being attracted to an ex-con, a man convicted of a third-degree felony? Is there some problem with that?" He taunted her as if it were a big joke, when in fact she knew he was deadly serious from the look in his stormy gray eyes. "Is that it? I want a truthful answer," he demanded. "I deserve that at least."

"I need time to think. I can't think straight when you're near me like this," she murmured, opening her eyes and blinking rapidly. "Everything gets elusive." She saw a smile crook the corner of his mouth. That seemed to please him. A smile spread slowly across his face, transforming him again.

"The same thing seems to be happening to me when I'm around you," he replied huskily. She wanted to laugh, but she stopped herself. It really wasn't funny, she thought. No, it wasn't funny at all. It was bizarre, and she couldn't seem to do anything to stop feeling about him the way she did.

"I'll call you," he said in his low, quiet, very male voice.

"All right," she agreed reluctantly. She hesitated. Then turned around. "Thank you for the dinner. I enjoyed it," she said rather inanely, but she wanted him to know that he was good company.

The following week, Laura avoided Quint like the plague. The rational, sensible part of her mind had taken charge, and when he called, she put him off. He called twice more, and twice more she found excuses. After that he didn't call again. She thought she had successfully discouraged him and settled back into the routine of her life. The days slipped by and nothing more happened. The weeks slipped by. She caught glimpses of him here and there. One day she was in the snack room getting coffee. She turned around slowly with a steaming cup in her hand and found him looking straight at her. Her hand shook, and she spilled hot coffee on it, but she was barely aware of it. Something remarkably like an electric sting seemed to arc between them. He said nothing. He simply stared at her and then turned and walked away. When she went out to the parking lot that evening he was standing there.

"Why are you running away from me?" he demanded.

"I told you we work together," she said quickly, and moved to get into Tina's car. Her own car was in the garage being repaired, so she was getting a ride home. He leaned on the door so that she couldn't open it. There was that hard, implacable expression in his eyes again, the one that he used when he wanted to hide his feelings from the world or when he was determined to get what he wanted.

"Do you ever think of me?" he asked, leaning back against the car with maddening indolence and lighting a cigarette.

"Those are bad for you," she said impatiently. She couldn't get in the other side of the car because it was parked too close to the wall of the parking bay, and he knew it.

"So I'm told," he said. "But then I don't pay too much attention to what people say. It's so seldom they tell the truth." He was really mad; she had succeeded in making him intensely angry. "I asked you a question," he added in that deadly calm, expressionless voice that needled her emotions.

Did she ever think of him? She almost burst into hysterical laughter. If she were honest, she would say that there were times when she seemed unable to think of anything else. The feel of his arms around her, his mouth on hers seemed to be imprinted on her mind and senses forever. A heat rush surged inside her whenever she thought of those moments in his arms. She turned her face, angling it away from him, so that he couldn't see the expression in her eyes when she answered him.

"From time to time," she said in an attempt to sound offhanded, to keep him from seeing the struggle that was going on inside her.

Suddenly his hand grasped her chin, and he pulled it around slowly to face him. The truth was mirrored in her eyes, and he saw it immediately. He towered over her, his overpowering physical presence so close she felt dizzy.

"I think you think about me a lot. And I'm here to say that the feeling is mutual." His tone implied that she knew how much that was. "Let me take you home."

"I'm supposed to be getting a ride with Tina. My car is in the garage."

"Tell Tina that I'm taking you home. That she doesn't need to give you a ride," he said matter-of-factly, as if it were an everyday occurrence and there was no reason on earth why she should do anything else.

They gazed at each other silently for a long moment. Laura knew instinctively that if she did what he suggested, she might set something in motion with a momentum that nothing on earth could stop. Then to her own surprise she did what he said and returned to the office.

Tina wasn't pleased that Laura had in effect cut her out with Quint. Yet she gave a resigned sigh and asked what happened to Laura's other boyfriend. As she'd invented the boyfriend, Laura invented a breakup. She didn't know what else to do. Things just seemed to be moving out of her control.

Quint drove her home in silence. At her apartment, he asked, "Can I come in and talk to you?"

"I don't think that would be wise."

"No, I guess it wouldn't," he murmured drily. "I want to see you again, that's pretty obvious." He stared though the windshield as if it were something difficult for him to say. "And I think you want to see me. But you're holding me off, and I'm not sure why." He paused and turned around to face her. "It's not because we work together." She watched him silently.

In her silence was a kind of unspoken agreement. He got out and opened the car door for her. They stood facing each other.

"Why don't you answer me?" he asked in exasperation. His narrowed eyes scanned her as if trying to see inside her head. At her imploring look he let out a sigh. "All right. I won't press you for the reason. But I want to see you again," he added with a slow grin and the confident male assertiveness that she guessed usually got him what he wanted.

She closed her eyes, trying to summon up the strength to say no.

"It would be better for you if we didn't see each other again," she finally replied in an almost inaudible voice.

"Why don't you let me be the judge of that," he mocked softly, not taking her seriously. "Would you like to go to a club on Friday? You seem to like to dance." His smile was wickedly explicit. She knew he was referring to the way she responded in his arms on and off the dance floor. Her face grew hot.

"Yes, I would like that," she admitted, looking back at him steadily, knowing that she had just tossed her last shred of sanity out the window. There was something about him that she simply could not turn away from. Was it the fear that she would never feel like this ever again in her life? Was that what made her throw all caution, all reserve to the wind?

"I'll pick you up about eight. Would you like to have dinner first?"

She nodded, still unable to tear her gaze away from his. He seemed to be equally absorbed by her. Neither one of them wanted to move away. Finally she called up some common sense.

"I have to go in now."

"See you on Friday." He grinned as he straightened and pushed away from the car.

Chapter 5

Laura counted the days until Friday. She saw Quint at work on several occasions. Twice he came into Jim Barnes's office, and when Mr. Barnes was busy rooting through his desk for something, Quint's eyes sought hers across the space of the office. Then Mr. Barnes surfaced and flourished in his hand some paper he had been looking for. Quint immediately turned back to face him, but not before his gaze slid hungrily over her, setting her blood on fire. Friday seemed aeons away.

Finally, though, Quint was at her door.

"You look great," he said, a husky note creeping into his voice. Given the impact of his dark gray eyes and that husky voice, she knew the words weren't spoken merely out of politeness. A rush of pleasure surged through her.

"I'm ready," she murmured. She made no other comment, but the curve of her soft mouth and the sparkle of feminine appreciation in her eyes confirmed their mutual admiration for each other.

"Let's go." His hand rested lightly but possessively at her waist as they walked out to his car.

The dinner was superb. They stuffed themselves on baked stuffed lobster and finished the meal with Strawberries Cardinal. Afterward they went to a nearby club to burn off some of the excess calories. When they reached it, they were both in high spirits, and as soon as Laura had placed her handbag onto the table, Quint pulled her immediately out onto the crowded floor. The current rock hit had an extremely infectious rhythm. Couples crowded onto the floor, and Laura and Quint soon were hemmed in and laughing out of sheer gaiety as the music pulsated all around them and flashing lights transformed the dancers into flickering surreal apparitions.

They danced until they were tired, and then a slow song came on. He pulled her into his arms immediately, as if he'd been waiting for the opportunity, and they began to dance slowly to the mesmerizing, haunting melody that insinuated itself into the atmosphere and altered the mood of the entire club.

Her arms slid up around his neck, and his hands went to her waist so that they were pressed against each other like two pieces of paper glued together. He buried his face into the curve of her neck and whispered into her ear how good she felt in his arms, and then she felt his body shudder against hers and his arms tighten around her. His lips brushed the side of her face with aching tenderness. They danced locked in each other's arms, barely aware of the people who surrounded them, until he pulled back and looked down at her. There was a hunger in his eyes that he made no attempt to hide.

"I could do with something tall and cool," she said a little shakily, in an attempt to break the spell and lighten the mood. She knew they had to slow things down. Things were happening so fast between them that her head was spinning.

"I'll get something at the bar. What do you want?" The expression in his eyes said if she asked for the moon he would try to get that for her, too.

"I'd just like a soda," she replied, smiling back at him, mesmerized by the look in his eyes. They stood there for a prolonged moment and then it seemed to dawn on him that he was supposed to be getting her a drink.

"One soda." He grinned with boyish charm and walked over to the bar.

She sat down at their table, unable to take her eyes away from him. She had never seen this side of him before. It was a new dimension, so different from the wary, suspicious, cynical one. Her gaze slid over him as he moved into the crush around the bar. She loved watching him. She was beginning to realize that she loved everything about him; every gesture, every mannerism, from the way he moved to the way he quirked his mouth when he pulled out one of his rusty grins. All that made him what he was, in fact.

She sat gazing at him, wrapped up in these amazing thoughts, until she saw a stocky man almost as tall as Quint move alongside him. Her thoughts about Quint were suddenly suspended as something inside her was alerted by the stocky man's presence. The man's arm reached out to slide across Quint's shoulder, but with wary adroitness Quint avoided it. Laura saw the expression on his face harden. His whole demeanor changed from one of relaxed pleasure to slowly winding aggression. Everything about him was altered; his expression became closed, his eyes wintry, his mouth cynical. She saw him unbutton his jacket as if he wanted to keep it from restricting his movements, and then he jerked his head in the direction of the alley as if he wanted the man to go out there.

Laura got up hesitantly and walked toward the two of them. The music was loud, but she could hear the unfriendly vibrations in their voices as soon as she approached.

Quint turned to her. "Laura, get back to the table. I'll be there in a minute." His tone was cold and incisive, that flat voice that allowed no room for discussion.

"What's this, Quint? You got yourself a woman?" The other man's gaze slid over her lewdly before turning back to Quint. "Do you still know what to do with one of those?" he taunted, jerking a thumb in her direction. "You didn't forget how while you were inside?" The man laughed uproariously at his own joke, but no one else was laughing.

Laura could see the dangerous gleam building in Quint's eyes.

"They say it's like riding a bicycle, man, you never forget how." The man laughed uproariously again, continuing to ignore the gathering storm in Quint's expression.

"Cassidy, if you know what's good for you, you'll shut your mouth. Before I shut it for you." Quint's voice was low and deadly calm, like the eye of a hurricane.

Laura didn't move, not because she didn't want to do what Quint had asked her to do, but because she found it difficult to move at all. She was frozen. The threat of physical violence always had done that to her, making her easy prey. Her gaze swiveled to the man called Cassidy. He wouldn't shut up. His gaze slid over her again.

"With that one you ought to remember real quick," he gibed again. "She looks real juicy."

"I think we should finish this conversation outside," Quint said in the same quiet voice that indicated a distilled white-hot anger.

"What's the matter, Quint? Lost your sense of humor or something?" The man backed away with his hands raised in the air in a falsely placating gesture, feigning surprise that he had offended in any way. "No harm meant, pal." His beefy red face broke into a leering, chipped-tooth smile, and Laura felt sickened.

Suddenly Quint reacted and with one hand seized the front of the man's shirt and propelled him through swinging doors out into the alley. Laura had to stifle a cry of alarm to keep from drawing any more attention. A few people had already turned around to stare. She quickly slid through the doorway and followed them out. Shocked into immobility, she saw Quint slam the man up against a brick wall. The enraged man drew a switchblade from somewhere and thrust it at Quint. The knife grazed his hand, and Laura watched in horrified fascination as Quint knocked it away and delivered two short, sharp jabs below the man's diaphragm and then rammed his knee into the man's groin. Cassidy let out a bellow of pain and slid down the brick wall to sit in a crumpled heap. Laura stared, transfixed.

"Let's get the hell out of here," Quint's voice exploded in the silent alleyway. He grabbed Laura by the arm, and they dashed to his car. Faint strains of rock music drifted from the club. All Laura could think of was that Quint might get into more trouble and that somehow it was because of her.

Quint pulled out into the traffic, and Laura saw that his bleeding hand had made red spots on the cuff of his white shirt. She began to sob quietly. The incident had dragged up dark memories she'd thought long dead.

When they reached her apartment, Quint flicked off the engine and turned toward her. That hardened, closed expression, the one he adopted when the world dealt him another low blow, was back in his eyes and face.

"I'm sorry, Laura. I'm sorry that you were subjected to that...."

He had gone back inside himself. The laughing Quint that she'd seen on the dance floor had withdrawn, replaced by the cynical man of steel.

"Your hand's bleeding," she murmured.

"It's nothing."

"Please let me clean and bandage it," she said. That was the least she could do for him.

The tiny apartment was warm and inviting when they stepped inside. Laura put her clutch bag onto the table and went to fetch the first aid box from the bathroom cabinet. When she returned, she saw that Quint had slipped off his jacket and that blood from his hand was now running down his arm into his sleeve. She unfastened his cuff link and rolled up the shirtsleeve as he stood silently observing her. Then she examined the cut from the knife.

"I wonder if we should go to the emergency room at the hospital."

"No, it's not deep enough for stitches. Take my word for it."

She felt he knew what he was talking about from past similar experiences, and his words stung her. She picked up the antiseptic and began cleaning his arm and the area around the cut. When the blood was cleared away, she was relieved to see that the wound wasn't as bad as it had looked at first. She quickly cut off some gauze and wrapped it around his hand. The gash ran across the palm. She concentrated, trying to remember what she had learned in first aid. She wound the gauze across the palm of his hand and around his wrist several times. As she maneuvered his hand, she talked in a low soothing voice, trying to get out of him what she wanted to know. He watched her with a bemused speculative tolerance.

"Why didn't you travel to another part of the country when you got out? Do you often bump into people who know you and about what happened to you?" She refrained from using the word *prison*.

At first he said nothing. His gray eyes were watching with a kind of studied indifference the way her soft hands wrapped the bandage around his. She stopped and waited for his reply.

"I didn't want to leave. I belong here. My roots are here. I didn't do anything wrong, so why should I go?"

"But isn't this painful for you, when you run into someone like Cassidy? How often does it happen?"

"Not all that often. I'm not running away," he stated tersely, as if it were something he had asserted time and time again. "I decided that a long time ago. In time people will forget."

If he had gone somewhere else, started over somewhere else, fate would never have been able to throw them together again so easily, Laura thought ruefully. Even though they had each picked a new town to live in—ironically the same town—they had both been too attached to this part of the country, both been too stubborn to leave.

She bent her head and cut the gauze, tore the end lengthwise, wrapped the ends around his wrist and tied them. She admired her handiwork and stepped back.

"Well, I think it's more or less what they taught us in first aid. At least the bleeding has stopped, and the bandage will keep it clean for a while. Is it going to be a problem when you get back to work?" She raised her eyes and looked at him. He was surveying her intently, thinking thoughts she couldn't read.

"It won't be a problem," he said in that low-pitched voice that seemed to have suddenly developed an edge to it.

She wondered if she had done something wrong. He seemed annoyed. Perhaps she had asked too many questions. His eyes were wintry as he gazed down at her.

"I'd better go," he said.

Something sank inside her. His words had a finality to them. She knew that he was right, that she shouldn't let him stay, and she made no move to stop him as he moved toward the door.

Laura returned to work the next morning, and for several days she didn't see or hear from Quint. Mixed feelings of relief and disappointment swept her continuously as the days rolled by. She kept telling herself that it was for the best, that it didn't matter. That this was what she wanted. She didn't want his continued interest, she didn't want to be attracted to him, she didn't want to feel the way he made her feel. But all the silent internal discussion did not change the way she did feel about him.

She missed him. She felt wistfully that she had lost something rare, something that didn't come along very often in life, something that possibly would never come again. She went through her work with the dull ache of longing for him in her heart.

Often she would stop in the middle of the day, and her mind would flash back to those moments she had spent with him, recalling the way he had looked at her, recalling the feelings he summoned from deep inside her that she didn't even know she was capable of. He seemed to plumb the depths and heights of her being. He drew on her and from her, and she found herself strongly aware of her desire to give him all he wanted and needed, and to take from him what he offered in return. But these bottled-up feelings were in glaring opposition to what her common sense told her she should want.

Then she plunged back into her work, telling herself again how lucky she was to escape because, sooner or later, the invisible time bomb that was ticking between them was bound to be triggered by something or someone and their relationship would explode into a million tiny pieces. She knew it and was as sure of it as she was of her new name.

Around noon, Tina ambled over and dropped to her customary place on the desk. Laura waited.

"How is Mr. Mystery Man? I hear via the grapevine that you have been seen with him on one or two occasions."

"Yes. But it's over." Laura turned to her typewriter, trying to give the impression that she was very busy and hoping that Tina would take the hint and disappear.

But Tina was not easily deterred. Once she had picked up the scent, she was like a blooded hound dog. "Why is it over?" she asked casually as she studied her fingernails with exaggerated interest.

Laura's lips tightened in frustration. Tina would not be satisfied until she heard it all. It was no use. Laura swung around on her swivel desk chair and faced her friend.

"We didn't hit it off. He's very nice. But we simply didn't click." Laura's green eyes were wounded and belied her words.

"Oh, really," Tina said. "He was not attracted to you, and you were not attracted to him. I see. And I suppose it was difficult to carry on a conversation with him, since he never uses two words when one will do."

"Very difficult," Laura admitted truthfully, thinking of how the conversation had continually veered back to his time spent in prison.

"So you didn't do very much talking. And now you are going to convince me that there was no—oh, what is the word I'm searching for? Electricity! There was no electricity, not even a spark between you."

"Absolutely nothing in that department."

"Laura, at lying, on a scale of one to ten, you are a minus one." Tina slid off the desk and patted Laura's hand affectionately, then turned to go.

She should have known better than to try to conceal anything from Tina, Laura thought ruefully. She reflected with a chill that once she had been very good at lying. Too good, in fact. She faced her typewriter and began to work with quiet determination.

At the end of the day, Laura gathered her things together and went out to the parking lot to wait for Tina. After a few minutes, Tina flew out of the office block and signaled to her, waving with abandon.

"Can you take the bus or catch a ride with someone else? I have to go to the hospital. My sister has finally gone into labor. I think she is going to have an elephant!"

Laura waved back, indicating with a nod that it was all right and smiling to herself at the prospect of Tina becoming an aunt. Then she trudged wearily to the bus stop. She stood staring unseeingly at the traffic passing by and thus, didn't realize the black Jaguar had pulled alongside the curb about fifty feet away.

She didn't care if the bus ever came. Life had become dull. Without Quint, it was as if a light had been snuffed out, a vital spark that gave her life luster, and now everything was dull and empty. All the joy in simple everyday things seemed to have somehow drained away. The food she ate was tasteless, the clothes she wore seemed to hang on her unappealingly, the programs on television or the books she picked up failed to capture and hold her interest. To top off her misery, it had begun to rain.

She heard someone call her name, and looked up vaguely. The voice barely penetrated her conscious mind, she was so deeply absorbed by her own thoughts. Again, she heard her name, and she looked up, frowning at the intrusion. Then she saw him striding toward her, and something spiraled crazily out of control inside her and her heart leaped with joy. Her face betrayed her emotions immediately and lit up with intense pleasure though she struggled in vain to hide it. When he saw it, a smoky look invaded his own eyes.

"I thought you might need a lift," he said in that low-pitched voice that had been echoing in her mind for the past week. Without hesitation, she walked toward him, he opened the car door and she slid inside as if they had some unspoken agreement. He climbed into his seat, and started the engine.

"Why were you taking the bus?" he asked.

"My car's still in the garage. It's old, and they're having trouble finding a part," she explained. She studied his profile, wondering why he had stopped to offer her a ride. The question must have been plain to see because he answered it.

"I wanted to talk to you." He edged the car into the stream of rush-hour traffic. They drove along, and she waited for him to say what it was he wanted to talk to her about. She didn't want to ask. She knew she should get out of the car and never see him again, that she should not encourage him in any way, but she couldn't seem to stop herself. She couldn't fill up the empty ache inside her, the longing to be with him again. And she couldn't stop the mad beating of her heart at the sight of him or the sheer happiness of being so close to him.

The car lurched to a stop in front of her apartment, and Quint switched off the engine and stared out the windshield silently for a long moment, still not saying anything. Laura began to think he had changed his mind. Her heart plummeted, and she reached out slowly for the door handle, unable to stand the exquisite torture of being so near without touching him and knowing it would all end in a matter of moments, anyway. He reached out instantly, and his hand covered hers.

"Don't go," he murmured huskily. Then he leaned over, and his hand slid underneath her hair and around the back of her neck. She watched him breathlessly as he lowered his head, brushed his lips over the side of her face and whispered into her ear. "Laura, I want to see you again. In spite of what happened the last time we were out. Will you go out with me again? I thought it was best if I didn't see you again. I thought you wouldn't even want to see me and would thank me if I did you the favor of staying away. But I can't."

Delirious happiness surged inside her when he told her why he had been holding off from seeing her again. It was because of what had happened at the dance club! She thought it had been because of something she'd done or because he simply wasn't interested in her anymore, wasn't attracted to her strongly enough to ask her out again. All the while, he had been convinced that she wouldn't want to go out with him again. If only he knew that the real reason she shouldn't see him again was her doing and not his. The knowledge struck some sensitive chord deep within her. As if he had in any way been to blame for the incident at the club. As if he had been to blame for anything at all. He was innocent and always had been. Relief and happiness shot through her in equally strong currents. Without thinking, her heart overruled her head.

"I want to see you again," she murmured softly, turning her head and looking steadily back at him. She saw a strange vulnerability flicker in his eyes, and then his hand tightened in her hair and he lowered his head so that his mouth found hers. He kissed her very hard and very long and then broke off the kiss and murmured against the soft skin of her neck close to her ear. The touch of his mouth sent a current through her that was devastating and made her press into him, her entire body a soft invitation.

"When?" he demanded, his hands tightening and drawing her up against him.

"When would you like?" she asked with a breathless catch in her voice. He moved back, and she watched him from underneath thick lashes, drunk with his nearness and the dizzying sensation of his mouth inches away. She was unconsciously provocative.

With swift retaliation his hand sank into her thick curling hair, and he teased her, tugging her head back gently so that her mouth was angled even more invitingly near his. His sexy gray eyes melted her.

"As soon as I can, you witch." Then he brushed her lips, softly this time, with infinite tenderness and trailed his hand down the curve of her neck. When he pulled away he surveyed the delicate lines of her face thoughtfully.

"How would you like to come flying with me?"

She stared at him blankly for a long moment.

"You haven't really got access to a plane, have you?" she challenged him with a disbelieving look.

A slow smile curved the corner of his mouth. He grinned at her triumphantly.

"I rent a Cessna twin-engine. It's great for getting away at the weekends."

"I'd love to go flying." She smiled, delighted by the invitation, knowing that he was an excellent pilot. She had heard Mr. Barnes sing his praises too many times not to believe it. So she agreed immediately when he suggested flying up to Orlando, to see Epcot Center.

Chapter 6

On Saturday morning Laura's alarm didn't go off
and she overslept. It was the pounding on the apartment door that awakened her. She hastily slipped on
her bathrobe, tied the belt and shuffled into the hall,
still half asleep. Opening the door a crack, she saw
Quint peering down at her.

"I'm sorry. Good grief, the alarm didn't go off! I
can shower and dress in thirty minutes. Promise," she
said quickly. "Help yourself to coffee in the kitchen,"
she shouted through the gap as she closed the bathroom door.

Quint's gray-eyed gaze followed her. He slid his
hands into his pockets and wondered what it was
about her that intrigued him so. He started to pull out
a cigarette and then reminded himself that he had
given them up. He leaned against the doorjamb,
slipped his hands into his pockets and thought about

Laura. Something about her nagged at the back of his mind, but he couldn't put his finger on what it was. All he knew was that he wanted her and he wanted to be with her. He wanted to experience those soft curves in his arms again, to breathe the musky scent of her when she was aroused and to feel the way she responded to him. It drove him crazy. And there was something else about her mixed in with all that femininity and vulnerability that drew him. She was intriguing. There was an elusive quality as if something was always held in reserve. For the hundredth time he wondered what it was. What difference did it make, he thought, and finally reached into his pocket and lit a cigarette. He was hooked on her, and he'd better take it a little slower and easier if he didn't want to ruin his chances with her. He was going to scare her if he came on too strong, if he unleashed the desire that was building inside him.

Prison had changed him. He was well aware of that. It had hardened him, made him more primitive. Prison was no place for sensitivities. It was like basic training in survival. All the baser instincts came out. Eat or be eaten. An eye for an eye. You learned to look after number one, and you developed a sixth sense about what was behind you. Your reactions were honed until you had hair-trigger reflexes. They had to be if you wanted to survive. It also made you take what you wanted when you wanted it. Restraint was a refinement of civilization. He reflected on how he had made a grab for Laura that first night when he kissed her, how much the niceties of civilization had been diminished in him. A few years ago, on a first date, he would never have come on to a girl like Laura as he had. But after the experience of being in prison, he had felt only a blinding need. There was something in her that he needed and wanted so badly, something soft and feminine and wholesome that made up for all the ugliness of what he had been through. When he felt the way she responded, he'd had to fight back his instinctive desire to have her, there and then. He didn't want that to happen again. He didn't want to lose her.

They drove to the municipal airfield and walked across the tarmac toward the area that was designated for private aircraft. Laura stood back as Quint paused beside a blue-and-white twin-engine Cessna and opened the cargo door. She passed him the tote bag she had brought along with her, and he stowed it away.

With a mischievous grin twitching at the corners of his mouth, he suddenly reached out, caught her around the waist and swung her easily up into the plane. Impressed with his strength, she had an alarming thought. Would he ever become aggressive toward her? Would he ever turn that awesome quicksilver strength on her as he had on the man called Cassidy? But as she slid into the copilot's seat, she realized she couldn't imagine him lashing out at her. She had seen him become aggressive only once, and that was when someone had attacked him. She had no intention of ever attacking him.

Quint swung easily into the pilot's seat alongside her, then closed the door of the plane firmly and latched it. He reached for the headset, and Laura sat quietly watching as he checked the instrument panel and went silently through a routine check.

"Have you ever been up in one of these things?" he asked, letting his gaze slide over her appreciatively.

"No," she murmured.

"Nervous?"

"Not with you." His eyes darkened fleetingly. She could see that her answer pleased him, but it had not been her intention to flatter him. She had simply stated the truth. She felt safe with him. That was unless he ever found out who she really was. The thought was like a dark cloud covering the sun, and she tried to conceal its shadow from flickering across her face. It was always there, she mused, no matter how happy she felt with him. The past was always there, insidiously threatening in the background.

"Good," she heard him reply in an offhand manner. Completely relaxed and unruffled, he asked the tower for instructions and then taxied the small plane to a nearby clear strip. "Let's get airborne," he said, and the plane immediately began to travel down the runway, quickly picking up speed.

Having already fastened her seat belt, Laura leaned back in her seat and watched the runway move by at an ever-increasing speed, accompanied by the roar and rumble of the plane as it surged and gradually lifted off the ground. She turned her head sideways to look out the window and saw the ground rapidly falling away, accompanied by the strong drone of the engine as the small plane soared into the fathomless blue canopy of sky.

With the ground disappearing below, her attention was inexorably drawn back to Quint. Conversation was difficult over the noise of the airplane's engine, so she was content to sit and observe what was going on.

She quickly confirmed what Mr. Barnes had said about Quint. Even to untrained eyes he had the look of a man who knew exactly what he was doing. He had the confidence of a pilot who had flown many hours and had experienced almost every kind of unusual situation in the air. She felt again the recurring sense of safety with him.

The thought was ludicrous, she mused, because if he ever discovered who she really was, she could only guess what his reaction would be. Would he be vindictive, she wondered, recalling once again the violence that was unleashed from somewhere deep inside him in the alley behind the club. She had watched in stunned fascination the swift, raw punishment he had meted out to the man who had pushed him over the edge. What would happen if she pushed him over the edge? Laura tried to put the thought out of her mind. What good would it do to worry about something over which she had no control? She was beyond the point of stopping herself from seeing him. She knew that now. She could no more stay away from him than she could stop breathing. A sense of fatalism settled over her. What would be, would be, she thought, and she felt helpless to circumvent it anyway.

Quint said very little, and they were soon circling over Orlando. The plane banked sharply to the left to line up with a runway. She was amazed at how little time it had taken to reach the city that played host to the vast amusement complex of Disney World. By car it would have taken several hours of solid driving. By plane they had made the trip in under an hour.

Quint glanced over to check that she was buckled in, and the plane began its descent, touching down smoothly and rolling down the runway, eventually losing speed and taxiing to a stop. After he had made all the mechanical adjustments and the routine checks, Quint leaped out of the plane, walked around to the other side and again lifted Laura down effortlessly to the ground. His hands slid slowly down her midriff to her waist, holding her longer than necessary, as if he were reluctant to let go. Laura was too aware of him looking intently into her eyes. His lingering gaze and lingering touch fired her blood.

The day was spent meandering the vast complex of Epcot, viewing the various exhibits in Future World, walking, talking, relaxing, just basking in the pleasure of each other's company. Quint's arm rested at her waist lightly as they explored the fascinating complex. At lunchtime, they stopped to eat at Alfredo's. Over the fetuccine, Quint probed about Laura's childhood.

"You said you grew up in Punta Gorda?"

"That's right," she replied, suddenly on edge. Any reference to the past immediately had that effect; it was born out of the fear that she might make a slip. His penetrating gaze seemed to swallow her up.

"Where did you live?"

"With my aunt. I think I told you that." She named the street.

"I had a friend who grew up in Punta Gorda. Maybe you knew him. He went to the local high school."

"He would have been years ahead of me," she murmured quickly to cover up another sudden surge of anxiety.

"True," he replied.

She was disconcerted by the casual enquiry, and then brushed it off. It was just one of those chance remarks, she decided, and thought nothing more of it. But the remark brought home to her the reality that situations similar to this would inevitably crop up from time to time and fill her with unease.

"Are you happy working at Cranston's?" she asked to change the subject. His countenance grew taut. She had the craziest desire to reach out and touch his face, to brush her lips over his, to smooth over all the rough times he'd had. His eyes skimmed her face as if he were reading her thoughts, and the burning look in them played havoc with her pulse rate.

"It's the best job I've had since I got out. At least I'm doing something I'm trained for and something I enjoy doing. I'd like to buy my way into a place like Cranston's one day, own a hefty share, get in on the management side of it, but still do some flying." He spoke almost as if he weren't aware of what he was saying as his eyes devoured the soft curves of her face in abstracted fascination. "My future as pilot with one of the major airlines was finished after what happened." His gaze moved down to the tender sensuality of her lips. "But I could conceivably own a share of a commercial venture like Cranston's. I've got quite a bit of money that my aunt left me, and one of these days I intend to speak to Barnes about it. But not until I've been there for a while longer. It's too soon." His gaze settled again on the curve of her mouth, and for one crazy moment Laura thought he was going to kiss her. But he went on telling her about his ideas, and she stared at him mesmerized by his unspoken touch, glad that he was putting back the shattered pieces of his life and relieved to find that at least some of the residue of guilt inside her drained away as he discussed his future dreams and plans.

They flew back after an idyllic day and arrived in Waverly as the light began to fade in the summer sky and the clouds were shot with crimson and gold and the palm fronds on the tall trees glinted like silver in the dying day. Quint swung easily out of his side of the plane and helped her down, capturing her against his lean hard body, letting her slide with excruciating slowness against his long limbs, so that she was aware of every inch of his lean, rangy frame. He bent his head, and touched his mouth against her forehead as he held her tightly to him, reluctant to let her go.

"Did you enjoy it?"

"Yes," she murmured, lifting her gaze to meet his. She had spent one of the best days of her life in his company, and she was now thoroughly besotted with him.

He lowered his head, brushed her lips with a teasing sensuality and then released her.

"I enjoyed it, too. I want you, but I also like being with you," he said quietly.

Deep pleasure, mixed with desire, surged through her. His arm encircled her waist tightly, and they walked to where his car was parked. They drove to her apartment block in companionable silence. When she looked at her wristwatch, she saw that it was almost eight o'clock. It was well past dinnertime, and she suddenly realized that she was hungry and that he must be, too. She turned toward him hesitantly.

"Would you like to come in for something to eat? I'm going to fix something for myself."

"Yes," he replied, a smiling curving his mouth.

Laura accepted that all common sense had vanished. She knew only that she wanted him with her and that nothing else seemed to matter now. Not even the fear that he might somehow discover who she was made any difference. It paled beside the overpowering desire to be with him.

Once inside the small apartment, Laura dropped her bag onto the sofa and left Quint lounging in the kitchen doorway as she went to survey the refrigerator.

"What would you like?" she called over her shoulder. "Chili and a tossed green salad or grilled steak, baked potato and vegetables. That's all I've got. Speak up, don't be shy."

"Steak and whatever goes with it, and I'm definitely not shy," he shot back. "I thought you had already discovered that."

Laura turned away from the freezer, thinking it was safer not to reply. She placed the steaks in the microwave to defrost them quickly, then started the potatoes. While the steaks were grilling, she made a salad. Quint stood drinking in the unconscious grace with which she moved around the kitchen.

"Would you like something to drink? I think I've got some wine. No beer, sorry," she said, checking the refrigerator again.

"Wine will do," he replied, not taking his gaze from her.

"We could always rent a video," she said. "There's a shop on the main road, or we could watch one I already have. Would you like to watch a film after we eat?'' she asked, unaware of the temptation of her soft, feminine sensuality.

''Are you trying to get me to stay?'' Quint teased.

''It was just a thought,'' she murmured. She hadn't wanted this wonderful day to end, but her face flushed at his remark. Now he probably thought she was being forward.

''Well, you don't have to do anything to get me to stay,'' he replied with a teasing grin. ''I want to stay, and I was going to figure out a way to get you to ask me to stay if you didn't.''

Laura tried to suppress a pleased smile as she reached into the refrigerator. Before she could turn around to place the bottle of wine on the counter, she felt him move up behind her and his hands slip around her waist. She drew in her breath sharply as he pressed her back slowly and intimately into his lean, rangy strength so that her soft curves were locked into his hard angles, into the cradle of his hips and against the long line of his legs. His breath fanned her ear.

''I've been wanting to do this all day,'' he whispered hoarsely, sliding his mouth down the soft curve of her neck.

Desire suddenly surged between them, and Quint turned her in his arms, pulling her yielding body to him. He removed the wine bottle from her hands, setting it down on the counter, then, locking her arms around his neck, he gave her a long, drugging kiss. Over the silent minutes, he dropped a succession of rhythmic kisses on her face, her mouth, her neck, until Laura felt herself falling into the familiar deep, dark abyss. Her hands grabbed hold of his shirt across his shoulder blades to counterbalance the sensation and then slid across the leanly muscled planes of his back as he parted her lips and deepened the kiss. His hard, powerful body seem to absorb her soft curves. The sensation was heady.

Suddenly, the buzzer on the microwave made her pull back abruptly, breaking off the drowning kiss.

Quint pressed his face into the soft curve of her neck. A ragged edge had developed in his breathing.

''The steaks,'' she murmured. She smelled something burning. She turned away from the look of raw desire in Quint's gray eyes and the ghost of a smile tugging at the corner of his mouth. He seemed to enjoy the disturbing effect he had on her.

She took the potatoes out of the microwave, put the steaks on plates, then served the salad in separate dishes. Quint uncorked the wine and poured some into fluted glasses. All the while, Laura tried to regain her composure and get the situation back to the mundane and away from the strong physical pull burgeoning between them.

Quint sensed her confusion, and when they sat down at the snack bar he steered the conversation to what they had seen at Epcot and to how easy it was to hop around the state in a private plane on the weekends, suggesting that there were lots of other places they could visit. They sat talking about the various possibilities over coffee. When they had cleared away in the kitchen, they went into the lounge and sank onto the overstuffed sofa. Quint slipped a video cassette into the VCR and Laura took off her sandals and stretched out to watch the film. After what had happened in the kitchen, she wanted to keep things relaxed between them, to keep the mad rush of desire at bay.

But it was not to be. Quint affected her like a heady wine, and her gaze slid over his lean, powerful frame as he sat sprawled on the sofa, his long legs stretched out in front of him, his sun-browned arms linked behind his head.

"Can you shift a little?" she murmured, maneuvering her legs behind him. She felt pleasantly tired after the long day.

He let her slide her feet behind him, and she leaned back and twisted onto her side to watch the film in the dimly lit room. Laura had seen the film before but it was a riveting one, and she lay absorbed, watching the movie until she felt Quint's hand drift along her leg and up her thigh. It was an unmistakable move, and she glanced swiftly at his face. His profile gave nothing away. But when he turned his head, the message of undiluted desire in his eyes was clear and unmistakable. She hesitated, not daring to breathe, as if balanced on some knife edge of self-control. He, too, seemed to be waging an inner battle with himself. Then slowly his hand slid farther to the curve of her hip and over the silky material of her bikini briefs. She closed her eyes, and her whole body shuddered at the sensations his touch aroused. She sensed him twisting around. Then he leaned forward and pressed his hard body against her softly curving one.

"Laura." His voice was husky and low-pitched. He lowered his head and found her mouth.

His lips were so warm, she thought dreamily. There was an utter gentleness in his lean, tough body bearing down on hers.

He deserted her lips for the soft curve of her neck. His mouth burned on the sensitive column as he whispered incoherent things. His potent yet indistinguishable words spread a wildfire inside her body. She moaned softly, and her hands slid to his shoulders, restlessly caressing him.

It was all the answer he needed. Something was unleashed inside them both, and he pulled her blouse out of her skirt and ran his hands underneath over the warm smoothness of her skin. As his mouth covered hers again, he unhooked her bra, pushed it out of the way and cupped her full, rounded breasts. He kissed her with a hungry rhythm that infected her instantly with his aroused passion. In no time at all they were locked in a restless writhing, maneuvering to get closer to each other as desire, shimmering like a palpable force between them, swamped their senses.

His hands became increasingly insistent, taking more liberties, exploring the soft roundness of her hips. The slowly burning desire that had ignited between them changed and took on a fervor and undeniable urgency.

Abruptly, Quint stopped kissing her, pulling her arms from around his neck and withdrawing. He stood up and turned away from her. She watched from the sofa, dazed as he drew in several long, deep, steadying breaths in his fight for control. Then he turned around and silently surveyed her.

"I'd better go, while I still can," he announced with a low-pitched grim determination to his words.

She nodded, still stunned by what had happened between them. "Yes," she said softly, her cheeks flaming as she stood up and awkwardly smoothed her skirt, which had worked its way up around her hips.

He watched her with a dizzying hunger in his eyes, and when she moved toward the door, he held up his hand. "I'd better see myself out."

She was grateful that he had the instincts of a gentleman and the strength of will to stop. She wasn't sure what had happened to her own sense of propriety. It seemed to have completely evaporated along with her common sense, she thought with dismay. Her gaze followed him out the door, and she sank back against the wall, suddenly frightened. She was falling hopelessly in love with him, and she was weary of living a lie.

The week flew by, and Laura wrestled with her conscience. Her thoughts trod wearily over the ground she had already traveled many times before. She tried to rationalize her behavior all over again, reminding herself that she had been under duress at the time of the trial, reminding herself of her youth and also of the fact that she had not been driving the car. She argued silently that she could not bring back those years he had lost out of his life. That he had to put the past behind him. And she told herself that she loved him, and she convinced herself that loving him might in some small way make up for his loneliness and help him to forget his past experience. She paced the rooms of her tiny apartment, going over and over every eventuality, constantly reminding herself that if he ever discovered the truth, it could wreck everything, it could destroy his feelings for her, it could tear asunder anything that they might build together.

But when all was considered, she came back to only one thing. She had fallen in love with him. Love was a ruling passion that overshadowed all else. But was she willing to gamble everything on it?

On Friday Laura met him in the parking lot as she was going toward Tina's car for her now nightly lift home. He called out as he walked toward her. Then, he just stood there in his silent, measuring way, towering over her, before finally saying, "Can I take you home?"

Out of the corner of her eye, Laura saw Tina coming. She should say no, she told herself. She kept willing herself to say no, but the word that came out was *yes*.

Just then Tina called out. "You are going home with him?" she teased.

Laura waved and nodded to her friend. Then she joined Quint.

"Your car still in the shop?" he asked.

"There's more wrong with it than I thought. And they still haven't tracked down the parts. It's going to take a while."

"Too bad."

"Yeah. Well, I don't mind taking the bus, and Tina's been great about lifts."

During the drive, there was silence between them. Laura felt the unanswered question that was hanging in the air. Were they going to go on seeing each other, and, if so, where would it lead?

When the car stopped at a traffic light, Quint turned to her. His gray eyes were bemused by some unnamed emotion.

"I was thinking of flying down to the Keys this weekend. We can rent a small yacht and go cruising for the day, do some snorkeling off the reefs. Would you like that?"

"I'd love to," she replied a little breathlessly. The idea that they could just take off like that amazed her. And the prospect of being with him for another entire day sent excitement and delight racing through her veins. They looked at each other for a long moment.

"Good. I was hoping you'd say that." He turned his attention back to the traffic and drove on with the ease and assurance he seemed to apply to everything.

Saturday morning finally arrived. The sun came streaming through the windows. This time Laura was dressed and waiting for Quint. She was wearing white shorts, a T-shirt, sandals and a straw hat with a wide brim pulled low over her eyes to protect her from the fierce sun. The Florida sun was always something to be cautious about, even when one had a tan. She heard the door buzzer shatter the morning quiet of her apartment, and she quickly zipped up the tote bag containing her swimsuit, a change of clothes, toiletries and towels.

Quint wore a navy T-shirt and white pants that clung to his long lean legs. Mirrored sunglasses obscured his eyes, so she couldn't read their expression. The breeze had ruffled his thick, dark hair, and his lean frame could have graced the cover of any yachting magazine, she thought.

"Come on, let's go," he urged, eager to be on the way. She gave the tiny apartment a last-minute check, then locked the door behind her.

They flew to Key West and went immediately to a marina. Quint had telephoned ahead to rent a small yacht. They stowed their food and gear on board and, with the aid of the auxiliary engine, moved away from the marina and then cruised out to one of the nearby reefs under sail. The white sails billowed and snapped overhead as an endless canopy of sea and sky surrounded them. Laura felt as though she had escaped into another world, freed from the humdrum pattern of everyday life, suddenly transported to a cerulean planet of pale blue sky and aquamarine waters and the gentle sway of the yacht.

She joined Quint in the cockpit and sat covering herself in sunscreen as he guided the yacht to a point not far from the reef they wanted to explore. After finding an anchorage, Quint announced that they would row a dinghy to the reef. It would come in handy when they wanted to rest from snorkeling, he added.

Laura slipped into her swimsuit with its plunging neckline and French high-cut sides, which revealed silky golden expanses of skin. She swept up her hair, tied it into a knot and slipped off her small hoop earrings. As she finished, Quint, in brief swimming trunks, emerged from below decks. They stood gazing at each other for a long moment. His sleekly muscled length towered over her.

"Ready?" he asked, his eyes still sliding over her in undisguised appreciation. She nodded briefly, and they climbed into the inflated dinghy, and Quint rowed to where they could see the reef directly below them. They both dove into the clear waters, plunging beneath the surface into a world of brilliant colors and strangely swaying gardens. The impact of it all stunned Laura's senses, and she gazed around entranced. Quint swam alongside, and they cruised the area easily, with their flippers propelling them effortlessly.

"It's gorgeous!" she cried as they surfaced.

"Watch out for the stinging coral down below. I'll show you which one. Whatever you do, don't step on it or touch it," Quint warned.

"Okay," she replied; and adjusted her face mask before they dove beneath the surface again.

Quint signaled to her which coral to avoid, then they swam for well over an hour, exploring the aquamarine deep, Laura pointing excitedly to the natural wonders that surrounded them.

"The brilliant red ones are snapper, and the one with large bulging eyes that followed us curiously is a grouper," Quint explained as they clung to the side of the dinghy, resting. "And those small ones with the brilliant stripes are called trigger fish. If there's a spear gun on board we can spear some later for our dinner."

They rowed back to the yacht for a late-afternoon lunch. When they had dried off, they went below decks to the small galley. Quint uncorked some light wine and tossed some shrimp into the steamer, and soon they sat down to enjoy salad, fruit, shrimp and rolls.

Nothing had ever tasted so good, Laura thought, closing her eyes blissfully. The sea, sun and salt air put a sharp edge on her appetite. She had always heard that and now was finding out for herself that it was indeed true.

Afterward they sat on built-in settees in the main cabin out of the blazing sun and listened to music from a tape deck. The music enhanced the blissful serenity of the day and the sensation that they were in another world. A world free of the past, Laura dreamed to herself. A simple and uncomplicated world with just the two of them floating in it, as in a gigantic transparent capsule. She felt she could stay there forever, perfectly content, if no one disturbed her.

"You swim well. Who taught you?"

"My sister—" The words popped out. She stopped short. Too late, she suddenly realized what she had divulged, and they were suddenly in treacherous waters again. To cover up her horrified expression, she ducked her head to take another sip of the wine.

Quint's eyes narrowed, and he studied her intently before he spoke.

"You never mentioned you had a sister." He was watching her closely, and she knew she had to come up with something quickly.

"Oh," she replied with embarrassment. "I never talk about her. It's because we don't get along. She lives overseas. We never see one another."

She saw his face lose its sharpened, suspicious look of curiosity. His wariness was easily aroused, she reminded herself, and was it any wonder?

She watched him lean back, resting one arm over the back of the settee as he stretched leanly muscled legs out in front of him again. His brief swimsuit left little to the imagination, and she couldn't help her gaze slipping in silent admiration over the long, clean lines of his body. She thought she wasn't being obvious about it, but he noticed.

"Like what you see?" He grinned with a teasing note in his voice.

Her face flushed slightly. "You're very good-looking. I'm sure you've had women notice it before."

"Yes, one of them who particularly admired me put me in jail."

She flinched and prayed he didn't see it. Their silent, serene world was again being invaded by the dark shadows of the past. She put her head back wearily, knowing it had been too good to last. She felt his eyes on her. After a long moment, he moved toward her, sliding over to where she was sitting, and removed the fluted glass from her hand.

"You realize what's going to happen if we keep on seeing each other like this," he murmured in her ear as his hands circled her waist and pressed against the bare skin revealed by the cut-out sides of the brief swimsuit.

Her eyes closed blissfully at his touch.

"I'm already having problems keeping my hands off of you. And it's getting harder all the time." He bent his head and kissed the sun-warmed curve of her neck and shoulder. She sighed audibly and clenched her eyes at the powerful response it drew from her.

"Laura." He whispered huskily in her ear and turned her into his arms so that she felt the hot urgency that suddenly danced between them as his mouth covered hers with infinite tenderness.

She kept her eyes closed and felt his sun-heated body against her own, unable to move as he slowly prized her lips apart with a long drugging kiss. Feeling her response, he pressed his body into hers, urging her back against the settee, nudging her legs apart. She groaned softly at the powerful sensations that began to eddy low in her body, and soon a fiery urgency grew between them, blotting out everything around them and wrapping them in a dark tunnel of desire that rushed around her, pulling her down into it. Vaguely she knew that she was kissing him back as wildly as he was kissing her. Intermittently he broke off the kisses and whispered his rough need and grasped her hips, rolling her against him with a hot, compulsive need.

Laura knew she had to stop him. Shadows of the past were there, between them. She couldn't forget her guilt or escape her fear, even now, like this. Suddenly she pushed away, slid out from beneath him and moved toward the companionway.

When Laura reached the deck, she stood there, her head tipped back to the sun, breathing in deeply to calm herself, trying to slow the pounding of her heart She had to use some self-control; the words kept banging away in her head.

Quint came on deck and plunged over the side into the water, perhaps to cool off the desire that had built with such speed between them. A few minutes later, he used the rope ladder on the transom to get back into the yacht, and he stood with water streaming down his body. His eyes studied the horizon, and then he walked over to where she stood. He stayed a few feet away, as if he didn't trust himself to get any closer.

"So you want to have some grouper for your dinner?" he enquired with an engaging smile.

"Yes." She smiled back. "Do you think you can catch one?"

They were both trying to put what had happened behind them, trying to pretend that things weren't rapidly spinning out of control.

"There's a spear gun over there. I used one some years ago and with a bit of luck, I haven't forgotten how."

Quint picked up the gun and climbed back down into the dinghy. Laura followed, and they rowed back to the spot they had explored before lunch.

They spent the afternoon trying to spear one of the groupers that prowled the area. Though the grouper isn't a particularly canny fish, the ones they saw somehow always managed to dart behind a rock at an inopportune moment. Nor did the spear gun function properly, and it was well over an hour before they were successful and Quint got two. They swam back to the dinghy and climbed tiredly into it.

"Oh." Laura collapsed onto the bottom of the rubber craft. "I'm not used to all this swimming. I don't know if I'll have the strength left to cook those fish."

When they reached the yacht, Laura lay on the deck, resting, as water streamed off her body into little pools onto the spotless teak deck. Quint got out a filleting knife and cleaned the fish. Then they went below decks, where Laura poured glasses of fruit punch over crushed ice and then collapsed onto the settee.

"We can stay overnight on the yacht," Quint said as he stood over her with the cooling drink in his hand.

Laura's eyes traveled slowly up the length of him, from his long, powerful legs to his narrow hips and leanly muscled torso and on up to his face. She knew what he was asking, and she knew what it would mean if she stayed on board. He would want her to sleep with him. That was perfectly obvious. Desire curled deep inside her. She didn't want to answer. Instead, she stood up and walked toward the galley to get some more ice for her drink.

"You know what's happening between us, Laura. Don't you? You know that sooner or later we're going to end up in bed together."

"Stop!" She covered her ears, not wanting to face up to the realities of their situation. What he said was true. She could feel it. They couldn't go on spending so much time alone together. They couldn't go on getting locked into passionate embraces. Sooner or later one of them wasn't going to have the strength of will to stop. She turned to face him.

"You're not a child, Laura. And I'm no saint," he said flatly. "I don't know how much longer I can hold off. I want you like hell. You must know the effect you have on me. It's taking all my willpower to stop when we start anything."

She was unable to think of a thing to say. She couldn't deny what was happening between them. It was useless to try.

His face grew serious. "It's not only going to bed with you that I've been thinking about. I've been thinking about a lot of other things, too," he added, his voice low-pitched and compelling.

"I've been thinking of *us* on a long-term basis, together."

"Stop. Idon'twanttodiscussanythinglikethat." The words shot out of Laura's mouth so fast that they all ran together. Quint turned and looked at her with a grave, perplexed expression in his eyes, and she placed her hands on his arms.

"Everything has happened so fast between us," she murmured in a soft, pleading voice, but even to her own ears the words sounded hollow. She had to stall, to hold him off, she thought frantically. She just couldn't deal with this.

"Do you want me?" he asked huskily. "I have to know. Because if you don't, I want to get out of your life. I can't be around you otherwise. And if there's somebody else, I want you to tell me. I want you, Laura, but I won't share you." His eyes watched her closely, reading her carefully.

"There's no one else," she murmured. She was very tempted to invent someone, but she knew she couldn't lie to him. She would never lie where he was concerned ever again.

"Do you want me?" he prodded intently.

"Yes, I want you." The understatement of her words mocked her. She could hardly think of anything else at times like this when he was near and her whole being seemed to cry out for him.

He looked at her speculatively. His gaze didn't waver. It was as if he were thinking very carefully about what he was going to say next. He was reluctant to say it; the cold expression on his face indicated that he was expecting rejection.

"I haven't talked about anything more, Laura, because I wasn't sure, what with my past experience, you would want anything permanent." He paused briefly before going on. "I thought at first we could have whatever we wanted on a casual basis. But I'm not made like that. I want more than that. I want you to tell me how you feel.'' His expression was grave, and he watched her closely for a reaction.

She was shaken by his words. Stunned. He didn't know what he was asking. He had no idea! For them it was impossible. And she couldn't even tell him why. She saw the handsome features of his face harden into the cynical mask he wore whenever the world dealt him another low blow. There was a sardonic flick to the corner of his mouth before he spoke. His gray eyes were hard and calculating.

''I can see the answer in your face. There's no need to explain.''

His words were cutting and derisive. All the tenderness and warmth that she had caught glimpses of had been concealed once again behind the inflexible mask he wore. The expression in his eyes tore at her conscience. She didn't want to hurt him again, but what else could she do? She couldn't encourage him to think of long-term commitments for the simple reason that she couldn't hide her true identity from him indefinitely. And she couldn't live a lie forever.

''Tell me, Laura. What do you want? A casual fling. Some really good sex,'' he drawled. ''I think I can accommodate you.'' His voice was deep and husky but with an edge of sarcasm. His hands bit into her soft flesh, and he yanked her toward him, kissing her with bruising intensity. There was no tenderness now. Her hands instantly seized the solid muscles of his upper arms, and a soft moan of protest rose in her throat.

She tore her head away. ''Please! That's not what I want, either,'' she gasped.

"What do you want?" he challenged, shoving her away, almost roughly.

She stood looking at him with a bruised expression in her eyes as she rubbed her arms where his hands had left red marks. She saw the quiet white fury of his anger blaze to the surface just as it had in the alleyway, and she saw him struggling to contain it.

"We'd better go back," she said, shaken.

"You still haven't answered my question."

"I can't answer you. I don't want a casual fling. You must know that."

"Then why in hell do you keep on seeing me," he demanded with soft menace, "if you don't want anything more than that?"

"Because I can't stay away from you," she cried. "Because I want to be with you all the time."

Her words must have had the ring of truth in them—they seemed to reverberate through him, and he stood convinced, his anger dissipating.

Quint moved forward and put his hands on her arms again, rubbing them gently up and down.

"We can put what happened to me behind us. It doesn't have to make any difference to the way we feel about each other."

Laura wanted to say yes, yes, I know we could. We could make a wonderful life together, loving each other and raising a family.

But all the inconsistencies, all the little lies and the attempts needed to cover up the past danced around in her head, and she knew somehow it would all prove futile. Sooner or later she would trip up.

"I can't explain," she said softly. "You'll just have to believe me when I say I can't help it. I don't want a casual fling, but I can't think of the long term with you. I wish with all my heart that things were different, but I can't change them.'' She beseeched him with her eyes.

His gaze bored into hers, and she sensed that he felt her anguish, that she had somehow conveyed it to him and touched a sensitive chord in him. She realized instantly that perhaps it was because at one time he, too, had vainly tried to convince people of the truth of something that, to all appearances, looked false. Perhaps some of the anguish he had known at the trial surfaced from deep inside him, reminding him of what it was like, and he sensed that she was telling the truth. That whatever her reasons for avoiding any commitment to him, she did care for him, she did want him; he knew that.

"Do you love me?" he asked.

More than anyone I have ever known, she wanted to say. But how could she?

Something flickered in his eyes, and his hands tightened on her arms once again. "Laura," he whispered hoarsely, and then he gathered her in his arms and began to kiss her with an aching tenderness, first her face, her cheeks, then her mouth as her arms came slowly around him and tightened.

She kissed him back softly at first, sliding her hands up the smooth skin of his back across his shoulder blades, pulling her softness into him, clinging to him. He groaned huskily and bent his head and gave her those insistent rhythmic kisses that set her on fire.

Gradually their need for each other began to take over, building a fiery urgency between them, racing between them like a hot current. He welded her to his frame, pressing her into his growing hardness and whispering hoarse incoherent things into her ears as he ground her hips against his. Their legs tangled in an urgent, restless need to get nearer, and his hands moved restlessly over her body, up and down her back in a fiery path.

Then he untied the swimsuit that fastened at the back of her neck and let it slide down the smooth skin of her body to her waist. His drugged eyes gazed at her as she stood in front of him, her breasts rising and falling with the aroused state of her breathing. She clutched his arms when she reached out to steady herself in this sea of desire that rippled between them, and he pulled her toward the master bunk.

Once inside the bunk he pulled her into his arms and pressed his face into the soft curve of her neck. "I need you so much. Want me?" he whispered raggedly.

"Yes." The word seemed to be dragged from somewhere deep inside her. When he drew back, his gray eyes were abstracted with aroused desire. As he pulled her back into his arms, his hands molded the soft flesh of her hips compulsively and intimately against him. He was fully aroused, and Laura gasped as he pressed his hard pulsing need in her.

Quint put her on the bed, and his fever-slitted eyes gazed down over the swell of her breasts, her small waist and curving hips to the tantalizing triangle, down the long sweep of her legs and back up again. He lowered his hard, toughened masculine body over her soft curves and pressed his face between her breasts. Boneless and pliant, Laura was drowning. She closed her eyes as he turned his head, teasing her sensitive taut nipples, his hands sliding beneath the curve of her hips and holding her locked under him. She felt desire shudder through his lean length just as it surged through her and made her ache to have him inside her. He lifted his head and murmured huskily in her ear what he wanted to do to her. Parting her lips, he kissed her and thrust deep inside her. Laura shuddered, and Quint's tenuous hold on control snapped.

All hell seemed to break loose. It was a wild joining together, her long legs tangling with his in a desperate need to get closer. Quint's body contracted again and again and again. Laura's senses sank into an iridescent world of breathtaking sensation. All inhibition fled as her mind centered on the white-hot excitement building inside her. Her hands clenched his sleek powerful shoulders as he drove into her with frenzied need. His body plunging deep inside hers created a torture so exquisitely intense she couldn't stand it. His incoherent exclamations rent the air. His velvet thrusts drove her to the edge of sanity until, together, they reached the highest peak of release and the very air seemed to explode around them. Quint's body pulsed into hers as he buried his face in the soft curve of her neck. His long fingered hands clenched the soft curves of her hips spasmodically to him. His labored breathing rasped sharply in Laura's ears.

Laura lay drifting with her eyes closed, floating on a sea of utter tranquility; Quint's body, spent, quivered with aftershocks. They lay in that quiet pool of oblivion for long, blissful minutes, neither one wanting to say anything or to move. Finally Quint stirred, rolled over with an animal grace and lay on his back with one arm tossed over his eyes.

"God, what you do to me," he breathed raggedly. His hand slid to hers and clasped it as his breathing trailed softly back to something resembling normal.

Laura was still in a state of stunned, heightened awareness, awakened to a world of indescribable pleasure. It was only Quint who had the key to unlock it. She wondered if it would be possible to achieve again, thinking that it had been some rare elusive thing that surely only happened once in a lifetime.

Quint rolled over again and gazed down at her with lazy eyes. The fire had been banked, but it still flickered, waiting to blaze again. He slid his hand underneath her jaw and up the side of her face, and bent his head and kissed her softly on the lips. When he looked again into her bemused eyes, she was staring at him in silent wonderment.

"This changes everything between us. Now we know where we stand," he said with a trace of huskiness in his voice. "What we've just had. It's like a drug. We'll want it again and again. I won't be able to stay away. I'll want you all the time now." He kissed her again, his tongue darting inside her mouth, his hands sliding over her soft curves, over her breasts with a now-familiar possession. And soon his body began to quicken, and their legs intertwined, and the tender kisses became more insistent and then urgent as they once again canyoned and climbed in that iridescent world of pleasure, lost in each other.

They spent the night on the yacht, and much of the next day, cruising back in the afternoon and flying back to Waverly before nightfall. Though they were comfortable together, they were both lost in their own thoughts, not saying much. Each wondered how this new dimension between them would affect their lives.

Laura tried not to think too much. It was dangerous to do so, the way things were. In the car, she leaned her head back and closed her eyes and dozed until they reached her apartment. Quint helped her with her bag and walked her to the door. There, he stopped and kissed her hard and long as if he didn't want her to forget for one minute what there was between them.

"I'll see you at work tomorrow. Can I take you home and come over in the evening?"

Laura nodded, completely besotted by the look in his eyes.

"I'd better go now or else I won't go at all. I want to come in with you, but I keep telling myself to hold back, not to rush you."

His words brought an ache deep within her. She wanted to invite him to stay. She knew what he said was the truth, because she felt her whole being responding instantly to his touch, as if every nerve ending in her body had been acutely sensitized, finely tuned to him, and she knew she was putty in his hands. Whatever he wanted, she wanted, and she simply couldn't think straight when he was around—she thought with her heart, her senses and her body. Common sense seemed to only enter when it came to hiding her true identity, and that was more a kind of desperate cunning rather than judgment.

She waved goodbye to him and disappeared inside the darkened apartment.

Chapter 7

Something tells me that you had a very nice weekend," Tina said the next morning in the office. "Could it be that sparkle in your eyes?"

"I did," Laura replied, and tried to suppress a ridiculous curl at the corners of her mouth, making her want to smile all the time at everything like a loon. People would think she was mad if she kept on grinning, she thought. But she had awakened this morning with the feeling that life was exceedingly wonderful and that she was floating in some kind of crazy bubble of delight. Everything seemed delightful.

"Could it have anything to do with a certain Quint Jones, I wonder?" Tina tapped a pencil on Laura's desk with idle speculation.

"Maybe," Laura replied. She tried unsuccessfully to make her expression grave and to look Tina in the eye.

"I think I'm getting the picture. And what has Mr. Quint Jones done now?"

Mr. Quint Jones had done everything now, Laura thought, smiling yet again.

"We went to the Keys and cruised and snorkeled, and it was just marvelous, absolutely marvelous. I'd never been snorkeling around a coral reef before. The beauty of it astounds."

"The cruising and the snorkeling left you breathless and panting for more. Are you sure that was all that made it so unforgettable?"

Laura's face flushed slightly. "That was part of it," she murmured hastily, looking down at some papers on her desk.

"Is this getting serious? Is he serious, or is he just out for a mad fling?"

"It's getting very serious." Laura conveyed just how serious by gazing helplessly at her old friend, as the whole dilemma rose up in her mind and the specter of what she was going to do about it hovered over everything, unanswered.

"I'm not really a mad fling sort of person," she added quietly.

"I know that. But what about him?"

"Neither is he." Laura wanted to end the conversation, keep it from going any further, check it somehow. "Everything has happened so fast. We both need time to think."

"Too much thinking can sometimes be dangerous," Tina replied. "Well, I must go and do some work. I'll see you at lunchtime."

Laura watched Tina disappear behind the bank of plants surrounding her desk and then got busy organizing her day. She tried not to think too much about Quint, but when she was not absorbed in her work, he inevitably crept into her mind, uninvited. She didn't know where their feelings for each other were going to lead. But she knew she didn't want to let him go. It was impossible for her to even consider that thought now. She decided that the best route was to take it one day at a time. Because she simply couldn't think of anything else to do.

After work Quint was out in the parking lot, waiting as he had said he would be. Laura's heart danced at the sight of him leaning against his car, looking for her. She bid Tina farewell as soon as she saw him. Tina, needing no explanations, waved cheerfully back to her.

"I'll see you tomorrow," Laura called as she walked away. Then she turned impulsively. "What did your sister have? You never told me."

"A baby boy. Nine pounds, three ounces," Tina said, rolling her eyes.

Laura smiled and turned around to Quint, who opened the car door for her.

"Barnes wants me to go on night flights all this week," he announced in a voice laced with exasperation. "That means I can't see you. I'll be flying every night this week. It's a special contract."

They looked at each other hungrily.

"I want to be with you," he said quietly, "but it's impossible."

"I'll see you on the weekend," she replied, unable to hide her disappointment. "Maybe it would be best if we didn't see each other for a few days. It will give us a chance to think things out more objectively."

"Will you think over what we talked about? I don't want a casual affair any more than you do. I want to see my engagement ring on your finger. Will you give it some thought? I'm sure we can work out whatever it is that's worrying you, Laura," he urged. "Almost any problem can be solved when two people talk things over in the right frame of mind."

His gray eyes held her pinned, earnestly drawing her into the potency of his masculinity, which held her mesmerized. Her eyes slid over the high cheekbones and lean contours of his face, his dark hair ruffled by the late afternoon breeze. I love you, she thought. I love you so much. I don't know quite how it happened but I can't imagine loving anyone more than I do you.

Laura leaned forward and brushed his lips with her own.

"I want you to remember something," she said. "Whatever happens between us, I love you. I want you to remember that. Will you always remember that?"

His gray eyes narrowed quizzically. "If you love me, why can't you make a commitment to me? I don't understand. Laura, what is it?" His hand slid to her jaw and clasped its delicate contours, and his eyes searched hers for an answer. But she withheld it.

"Damn it," he swore softly underneath his breath. "We shouldn't have any secrets from each other if we love each other. Promise me that you'll tell me what it is when I get off this night run."

She stared at him, frozen. Don't make me do that, her mind cried out.

"Promise," he demanded, his hands clenching tightly on her upper arms.

"I promise." The words popped out, and she wished instantly she could call them back.

That seemed to satisfy him. A smile tugged at the corner of his mouth; lines crinkled at the corners of his eyes.

"I know we can sort it out, whatever it is. You're probably blowing it up out of all proportion." He bent his head and kissed her with a long, coaxing kiss that drew an instant response from her so that he pressed her into him and then kissed her again, his hands sliding over her soft curves. Then he broke abruptly away.

"I've got to get back," he murmured in that voice that seemed to drop a notch or two when he was aroused, that sounded husky and almost rusty from disuse. He started the engine with an impatient flick of his wrist and drove swiftly out of the parking lot and through town to her apartment.

"I'll call you as soon as I get back," he promised as he helped her from the car, his eyes darkening with intent. Then he turned and climbed back into the car and drove away.

All that week Laura worked hard, relieved to have something to absorb her for long periods of time. But always in the back of her mind was the worry of coming up with some explanations for Quint. She tried to put it away from her, but it kept returning with painful anxiety.

She thought of how she would broach the subject. She could work her way into it and tell him first something about her family life at that time, explain

some of the extenuating circumstances that led up to
perjuring herself in court. She would tell him about
her loyalty to her sister, how they had always been
close growing up, especially when their stepfather had
come into their lives. How they had stood up for each
other against his violent mood swings. How they had
always tried to cover up for each other when something had gone wrong. How Connie had come to her
rescue that awful day. She could tell him, too, she
thought, about how they'd reacted in different ways to
the pressures and strains of this unhealthy situation.
How her sister had become restless and wild, always
out with a different boy, gradually getting wilder as she
grew older, while Laura had gone completely the opposite way, withdrawing into herself and fading into
the background.

Should she even try to tell him all this? Would it do
any good at all? she wondered miserably. Would he
even listen? And then, when she had prepared him, set
the stage, so to speak, trotted out the awful unpalat-
able truth of how both she and her sister had lied,
perjured themselves in court—what then?

She had seen the two sides of his personality, the
warmth and tenderness and deep passion he was capable of, and the hard, flinty sudden anger that sprang
from some hidden well within him. She remembered
the incident with the man called Cassidy, who had
heckled Quint in the club. Though her instincts told
her he would never take his aggression out on her, the
way her stepfather had, her instincts offered no assur-
ances about what might happen to the feelings he had
for her, the desire that surged between them, the pas-

sion they felt for each other. Would his anger extinguish those feelings? Which would be the stronger?

She ran a hand through her hair. She didn't know the answer. She couldn't even guess. She couldn't even imagine him being able to care for her after discovering the truth. She pushed her hand over her eyes, as if to rub away the weariness that all these dark, disturbing thoughts brought on.

She had to tell him, she concluded. She had to tell him. But she couldn't imagine losing him, or, she should say, she couldn't imagine living without him. But they couldn't go on this way.

Why not? temptation asked. Many people had affairs. She sighed and knew she wasn't made that way. She wanted marriage and all that went with it. And from what he had told her, so did he. She couldn't live a lie. No matter what it cost. Let him know, she decided, and then face the consequences. Her mind was made up.

The days passed in swift succession. On Friday, anticipation spread through Laura like a fever. She knew she'd be seeing Quint soon. Her heart skipped a beat, and her steps were quick and light as she walked toward the parking lot, completely forgetting about her resolve to explain everything to him. Only the pleasure of the prospect of seeing him again, having him near, surged inside her. Being with him overruled every other feeling.

She walked briskly toward her car. The garage had finally located the needed parts and had repaired it, and she didn't need a ride home from Tina anymore. She saw a tall, striking-looking woman leaning against one of the cars near hers. She seemed to be waiting for someone. Laura's gaze slid over the woman's short, stylish cap of red hair, her smart pearl-gray dress, her elegant, expensive shoes. There was something familiar about her, and Laura wondered vaguely where she knew her from.

As Laura drew nearer, her heart began to bang and pound ominously against her ribs in rising fear. Flashing warning lights and alarm bells seemed to be going on and off in her brain. Her worst fears had materialized as the tall figure moved away from the car and came toward her.

"Cathy, honey! Cathy, is that you? My God, I can't believe my eyes," she said, tossing down her half-smoked cigarette and crushing it.

Laura stood dazed and sickened with shock as her sister moved forward to greet her, throwing her arms around her and squeezing her in a bone-crushing embrace.

"I would never have recognized you! You are completely unrecognizable," Connie exclaimed, and stepped back to inspect her. "The only way I knew you was from this picture you sent me." She produced a tattered snapshot.

Laura squeezed her eyes shut in mortification. With a sharp pang of regret she remembered sending that snapshot on impulse. Someone, she didn't remember who, had taken the snap of her in a new bikini at the beach last summer, and, feeling proud of her pin-up figure, she had enclosed it in a letter to Connie. She hadn't thought of the possibility of Connie returning to visit. She'd never bothered to before, not in all these years.

"How did you find me?" Laura asked weakly, already knowing the answer.

"Aunt Margaret, the old witch, told me you were living in Waverly and working at Cranston Aviation. She said that you had changed your name, and when I asked, she gave me your address. The janitor at the apartments told me where Cranston's was, and then I took a cab and waited out here. I figured you'd get off work soon. Wait a minute, I've got a cab over there. Now that you're here, I'll let him go." She disappeared for a few minutes, and all the while Laura struggled to keep her wits about her as rising panic attacked her. Connie returned, and Laura noted she still moved in her own inimitable way that drew passing male glances.

"Oh, it's so good to see you," Connie said. "You look wonderful. I always knew you'd grow up into a raving beauty, and I wasn't wrong. But then, I'm hardly ever wrong, am I?" she teased, laughing softly.

But it's not good to see you! Laura wanted to cry out, still reeling from the shock of her sister's sudden appearance in her already turbulent life. Everything suddenly got misty around her. Her mind struggled to assert dominion over her stunned emotions, and then she began to react, and to react swiftly.

"My car is over there," she said, pointing to it. "Let's get going. We've got a lot to talk about." She must get Connie away from here as quickly as possible, before Quint turned up, before she gave away everything. Laura opened the door of the car and glanced furtively around. Her face blanched as she saw Quint striding from the far side of the parking lot, obviously heading straight for them.

"Get in," Laura prompted.

Alerted by the anxiety in her voice, Connie glanced up instantly.

"What's the matter, Cathy?" she asked, a frown of puzzlement crossing her beautiful face.

"Whatever you do, don't call me Cathy," Laura whispered, and quickly shoved her inside and hurried to follow her. Having spotted her, Quint began to jog across the parking lot toward them.

Oh, God, please don't let him see us. Please, Laura thought fervently as she fumbled with the key in the ignition, trying desperately to get the car started and to get away before Quint could catch a glimpse of Connie in the front seat of the car. Laura twisted the key in the ignition. The car stalled, the engine dying. She had to quell a sob.

"Please start. Oh, please start," she whispered to herself. The engine caught on the second try. Laura put her foot down on the gas pedal and the car lurched forward. She twisted the wheel to swerve away from Quint, but it was too late. She saw his gaze sweep over her, and Connie and she saw the look of stunned recognition surge across his face as the car sped on out of the lot.

Quint stood riveted to the spot where he had stopped running and watched the car disappear into the heavy evening traffic.

Laura didn't look back, she couldn't bring herself to. She drove at a fast clip, her eyes filling with tears as Connie's speechless gaze stayed riveted on her face.

"Has my coming to visit upset you? I didn't mean to upset you this way." She reached into her handbag and pulled out another cigarette and a gold, monogrammed lighter. "Or is it something else…Laura?" She hesitated over her new name Laura noted, as if uncomfortable with it but intent on using it because she could see Laura was deeply disturbed and she didn't want to upset her any more.

Was she upset? Laura's mouth twisted into a grim smile at what had to be the understatement of the century. Coming from Connie, it made her want to laugh hysterically. Connie thought she was all choked up about her returning. She didn't know that the man standing back there in the parking lot, the only man she had ever loved and possibly might ever love so completely, might have just discovered, judging from the look of white shock on his face, that *she* had helped to put him in prison. Not only helped to put him in prison, but had also altered the whole course of his life, taken some of the best years of that life, besmirched his reputation and made it impossible for him to get the kind of job he really wanted after years of vigorous training. And the woman who was responsible for it all sat beside her, thinking Laura was all choked up with sentimentality over seeing her sister again. The cruel irony struck her, unhinged her momentarily so that she began to laugh and cry at the same time. Tears rolled down her face, and it was all she could do to drive the short distance to her apartment. Connie looked at Laura as if her sister had taken complete leave of her senses.

"What in God's name is the matter? I don't know whether you're laughing or crying."

"Neither do I, neither do I."

They drove the rest of the way in silence. Finally the car cruised to a stop in front of Laura's apartment.

They got out of the car and as they walked toward the building, Laura looked furtively over her shoulder, praying that Quint hadn't followed them in some blind rage. It looked as though he hadn't. She breathed a sigh of relief. No one at Cranston's seemed to have taken much notice, and she hurried Connie inside the tiny apartment, glad of the sanctuary it provided. Once inside, she slammed the door and walked across the room in agitation and then swung around to face her sister.

"Connie, why did you come here?" Laura whispered, sinking back into the overstuffed sofa. "I told Aunt Margaret not to tell anyone where I was," she added fiercely, as anger surged inside her. They could never rely on Aunt Margaret for much, but she thought she could rely on her to keep quiet. She had thought she could trust her.

"Well, I'm not just anyone," Connie pointed out. "I am your sister, in case you've forgotten. And I wanted to see you." Connie took a deep drag on her cigarette and crushed it out in the nearest ashtray.

What on earth for? I don't want you here, Laura wanted to shout, but she held it in.

"I've left Bob," Connie said quietly, her face very still, not a glimmer of emotion showing through. Laura reflected that Connie was still as tough as nails.

"What do you mean, you've left Bob?" Laura asked with growing dismay.

"Let's just say that I can't live with him anymore. I've tried, and it doesn't work. I should have trusted my instincts and never married. I strongly suspected that I wasn't the marrying type. Can I stay with you for a while?" she suddenly asked.

"I helped you once, Connie," Laura whispered, "because you helped me. I felt I owed it to you, and because of that loyalty and because of my fear of Les, I did something terrible. I testified under oath that I saw Quint Jones driving that car when you left to go on a date with him. Both of us know you were the one behind the wheel." She could see that Connie remembered all too well. "I did something I shall never be able to forget. Please don't ask me to turn my life upside down again. You don't know what you've done by coming here," she murmured distractedly. "You may have spoiled something I wanted with all my heart. But I knew that it was hoping for too much…sooner or later, something like this was bound to happen, so I guess I can't really blame it on you."

Connie moved closer, intrigued and curious and not without a certain amount of worry. Where Laura was concerned, in spite of Connie's tough veneer, there was a soft spot.

"What is it, honey? You can tell me. I'm sorry. I'm really sorry about what happened in the past. It's played on my mind over the years. But I was not and never will be a big enough person to do anything about it, so don't ask me to." She sighed. "But why drag all this up again? What have I spoiled by coming here? You were so upset driving me home, Ca—Laura. It wasn't because I turned up, it wasn't a burst of sentimentality over my arrival. I don't flatter myself that feelings are that strong between us anymore. It's been years since we were close."

Laura stared at her silently, knowing she would have to tell her. Connie had picked up the scent of her fear.

"It's about Quint Jones," she said baldly.

Connie drew in her breath sharply. "He must be out of prison by now. Has he found you, threatened to hurt you in some way? Has he come looking for revenge?" She shook her head. "No, you're Laura Reynolds now. Has my turning up here somehow destroyed your cover-up?"

The look in Laura's eyes must have spoken volumes. Connie rushed on. "That's it, isn't it? Quint Jones is somewhere around here, and he knows you, but he doesn't know who you really are. Now that I've shown up, you're worried he's going to discover your true identity." She smiled triumphantly. "Tell me it isn't so. One look at your face, and I know I've come close. You never could hide things from me for very long, even when you were little."

Laura gazed at her for an endless moment and then murmured in a low, anguished voice. "If only that was all it was, Connie. It's not only that he doesn't know my true identity. I've fallen in love with him, and he doesn't realize who I am."

Connie was completely stunned and speechless.

"My God!" she whispered. "What a turn up for the books. How on earth did that happen?"

"It's a long story," Laura murmured wearily. "I went out with him partly out of a sense of guilt, but partly because I was attracted to him. I never dreamed I would fall in love with him. It wasn't something I wanted to happen. It just happened."

Connie moved away and picked up her handbag, absentmindedly searching for another cigarette, as what Laura had just told her sank in.

Laura closed her eyes and leaned back, staring into space, remembering. "And that's not all," she added grimly.

"Tonight as I was frantically trying to get out of the parking lot, he was coming to meet me. He saw you with me. I'm certain of it. That's why I was trying to get away so fast. But we weren't fast enough. I'm positive he recognized you instantly. You haven't changed that much, Connie. Unfortunately you're still as beautiful as ever.

"Think for a minute, Connie. What would he think as soon as he saw you with me? It would only take seconds for him to put two and two together. He's not slow-witted."

Connie's eyes narrowed as she lit her cigarette and inhaled deeply. "Maybe he thinks I'm just a friend of yours. Did you consider that? He wouldn't necessarily automatically conclude that you're my sister. My God, Laura, you've changed so much since you were sixteen that even I didn't recognize you. How could he be instantly sure, beyond any doubt, that you are my sister, under those circumstances?"

"Maybe he couldn't. But he's awfully quick."

"Try not to panic. You won't know what he's thinking until he comes out with it. Meanwhile, can I stay here with you overnight while I figure out what I'm going to do? I have to hunt around for someplace to stay. After what you've just told me and after what's happened, I realize that I can't possibly stay here." She rose from the chair and walked toward the window.

Laura silently agreed.

"Connie, did you ever really think about what we did to Quint? You said it played on your mind. Didn't you feel any remorse?"

Connie whirled around. "Do you think I didn't. I'm not a complete monster," she said. "I liked him. But I liked myself more." She shuddered. "You just can't imagine—hitting that poor old man. And Quint was lying there, knocked out when his head struck the windshield. All I had to do was pull him over to the driver's side.... I was terrified of going to jail. I was terrified of what would happen to you. What's done is done. I can't turn back the clock. Neither can you, Laura. I've thought of it many times. I don't want to talk about it." She crushed out her cigarette.

"Let me stay here tonight, and by tomorrow I'll be on my way," she said almost inaudibly.

As Laura watched her sister, she knew that Connie was not without remorse and that she was not as hard as she liked people to think she was.

"It's better if you do go," Laura explained quietly. "I wouldn't want to be here if I were you if he does come around. I've seen his dark side. Being in prison developed an aggressive streak in him. I've seen him when he's angry. He can be lethal."

Apprehension shadowed Connie's eyes. "I can well imagine. Don't worry, I'll be gone. I'm all right financially. I'll have to get a job soon, but I'm not desperate at the moment. What I really need to find first is a place to live and then I'll look around for a job. I'd like to settle down somewhere near the Gulf, and I haven't decided exactly where that will be. Have you got any suggestions?"

"Why not try the east coast or the Keys."

"I think the east coast. The Keys are beautiful but very small-town atmosphere. Would it make you feel better if I were on the east coast?" she asked.

"Yes. I could come to visit you, but the distance would be reassuring, taking into account everything else."

They spent the evening becoming reacquainted and poring over real-estate ads and the next morning Laura drove Connie to the airport so she could take the shuttle to the east coast. Connie promised to call and let her know if she found anything promising.

Laura returned home, still slightly dazed from Connie's brief but explosive visit. Quint had made no effort to contact her. Connie's visit was over, but the damage was done.

Laura was deep in thought as she parked in front of the apartment building in a kind of remote control. It was only when she looked up that she saw Quint. Her heart somersaulted inside her chest, and she almost sobbed with relief.

He was leaning against the Jaguar, smoking a cigarette. His expression was as impenetrable as flint, and she wondered how long he'd been there. She slammed the car door behind her and walked toward him hesitantly. His sensuous gray eyes studied her, and the force of his tough masculine presence suddenly filled her senses.

He moved away from the car.

"We were supposed to meet last night. Do you remember?" he asked, his voice deceptively soft. "Or had you forgotten?"

She thought she saw a challenge in his dark, probing eyes. His lean, powerful body seemed to pulsate with tension, and she hurried along the path, as if intent on getting to the door.

"I...oh, yes," she murmured, regarding him from underneath dark lashes. "An old friend turned up out of the blue and...she wanted me to take her to find someone's house. I didn't see you anywhere, and I thought you hadn't got back in time, so we went on without you. And when you didn't call, I thought you'd been held up en route somewhere and couldn't make it back in time." She spoke in a smooth and, what she hoped was a convincing tone.

"I saw you," Quint said evenly. "Leaving the parking lot last night. I saw your friend in the car with you." The way he almost imperceptibly emphasized the words "your friend" sent a sense of alarm splintering through her.

"Oh, did you?" Laura tried looking at him with feigned puzzlement, feeling her pulses racing in time to the beat of her heart as if in some kind of frenetic dance. She struggled to be calm, to keep her face an impassive mask, as if the friend she had encountered outside of work was just some casual acquaintance who was hardly worth mentioning. She stood gazing at Quint, who suddenly looked dark and dangerous. She felt the flicker of his eyes over her and prayed that her face wasn't betraying what she felt.

"I know that woman." He spoke with deceptive nonchalance.

"Do you?" Laura replied faintly.

Suddenly he seized her wrist, dragged her forward.

"I hope to hell this isn't what I think it is, Laura. I have this crazy idea going around in my head. I'm hoping like hell that I'm wrong."

He dragged her toward the apartment door, and Laura's heart went into high gear as she guessed what was on his mind. He suspected. He more than suspected. He was almost sure, and he was waiting, hoping that she was going to tell him that he was wrong. With shaking hands, she unlocked the door, and they stepped inside. In the hall, he slammed the door shut and turned to confront her.

"That woman in the car that I saw you with, her name is Connie Turner." He waited for a long, probing moment.

"Yes, that's right," Laura replied softly, trying to brazen out what she knew was an increasingly futile position.

"How do you know her? I want you to tell me how you know her, Laura." He seemed to bite down on the words. And, under the intense probing of his dark stare, Laura began to experience a dizzying sensation. She had sworn she would never lie to him again. And here she was about to do it. The thought sickened her, but so did the idea of losing him. She couldn't lose him, she thought desperately, as a feeling of helplessness swamped her.

"I know her from Punta Gorda," she said. That wasn't a lie. She and Connie had gone there several times to visit their aunt. But it was lying by omission, and Quint's finely honed instincts didn't miss it.

He leaned forward and grabbed her arms to draw her up against him. Their faces were only inches apart, and he spoke in a very soft voice.

"Laura, I'm going to ask you this once and once only. I'm not ever going to ask you again, but I want the truth.'' He shook her with a kind of gentle violence.

A tremor shot through her body as she gazed into the face of the man she loved, the man she was terrified of losing, but she knew she couldn't lie to him. Her words caught on a slightly breathy sob as she lowered her gaze and, almost inaudibly, she answered.

''She's my sister.''

The lean lines and contours of Quint's face froze into a harsh, rigid mask. His eyes darkened as his pupils dilated from the shock of her admission. This was quickly followed by an unwinding of some indefinable potent emotion, accompanied by an antarctic freeze in his eyes and demeanor that was indescribable. He thrust her away from him abruptly.

''Damn you,'' he said with a strange, strangled huskiness in his voice. ''Damn you to hell.'' He turned and left, slamming the door so hard that the whole apartment reverberated with the sound. Laura heard the screech of tires in the driveway and put her hands to her face as tears flooded her eyes and sobs racked her body.

Laura lived in a kind of limbo after the confrontation with Quint. She spent most of Sunday wandering around the apartment, barely knowing what she was doing, staring into space for long periods of time. She was afraid to contact Quint, and he made no effort to contact her. She went mechanically through the day wondering what she could do, if anything. Her thoughts chased one after another in circles, and her mind came up with no answers. There were no answers. Everything was finished between them. She was sure of it.

The squash courts were all busy in the huge gym. Dave Grant hurled the ball against the wall in frustrated angry defeat and then stood with his head bent, contemplating the strings of his racket for a long moment. He raised his head and stared at his partner, Quint Jones. Quint waited to hear what he had to say.

"Man! You play like you really got it in for somebody. It's not just a game of squash you're playing today, is it? I've never seen you play like this. You're usually good, but today you're deadly."

The squash courts echoed all around them with the squeak of shoes on gleaming hardwood floors and the slam of rubber balls into the walls of the various courts that surrounded them. Hoots of derision followed in the wake of some of the worse shots.

Quint and Dave had just finished their last game, and Quint won for the third time in succession. Quint knew there was a deadly look in his eyes, that flat, opaque look riddled with aggression that he had developed in prison. Dave's words hardly penetrated his thoughts. His mind was on Laura. The scene in the parking lot outside Cranston's kept flickering through his consciousness with relentless repetition. He couldn't get it out of his head. It kept flashing through his mind repetitively, like one of those squash balls ricocheting off the wall, making him play with a kind of ruthless rage.

Connie Turner sitting there large as life in the car as it drove by. Connie Turner sitting next to Laura. Connie was Laura's sister. The one she had mentioned who lived overseas. It had all come together in his mind in an insidious flash when he confronted Laura. He had halfway guessed at the truth, but had hoped like mad it was just a crazy, wild idea. But that had not been the case. Laura's confession had torn into him, leaving a deep gaping hole in his spirit, a mortal wound to his emotions. Laura was Connie Turner's sister! Damn, how had he not recognized her? She had looked so different then. In truth, he had barely noticed her. She had been one of those withdrawn, quiet types. Even now his memory of her and how she looked then was vague. It had been Connie who had held his attention at the trial. It was Connie who had attracted his undying enmity, it was Connie, not her shadowy sister.

That pale, shy, slender completely forgettable girl had turned into a bewitching, intriguing beauty. She had been nothing then, and suddenly she had become everything. What a complete fool he had been, pouring out his heart to her, acting as randy as a teenager whenever she was around, hardly able to keep his hands off the little bitch who had helped to put him inside. If she were here, he would wring her beautiful neck. It was a good thing she wasn't here, he thought darkly, picking up the ball and slamming it against the wall with his racket.

The ball spun away from the wall and out of control and Quint bent to pick up the terry towel on the bench and wipe the sweat from his forehead. He wouldn't be responsible for his actions if she were here. Dave watched him in silent speculation.

"Whoever is she, Quint? Are you sure she's worth it, pal?"

Quint gave him another deadly stare. Dave held up his hands. "Sorry I asked. I'll keep my mouth shut. What about a drink? I sure could use one. What about you?"

Quint flicked his head in the direction of the locker room. "I'm going to go and get cleaned up, and then I'll meet you for a drink."

"Okay," Dave said, swinging his racket off the bench and heading for the showers himself. "I'll meet you in twenty minutes at the bar."

Quint watched him go and stood lost in thought for a moment before he moved mechanically toward the dressing rooms. Self-derision continued to flow through him in angry waves. He reflected on the way he had pursued Laura. No wonder she had almost jumped out of her skin whenever they had met. He had to admit to himself that he *did* go after her. He had certainly done the chasing; she hadn't pursued him. No, he had to concede that. He'd wanted her the first time he'd met her. He couldn't pin that on her. With that angelic face and lush figure, she'd mesmerized him from the first instant he had bumped into her in Jim Barnes's office. And now what? he asked himself. The dark thought meandered in his mind. He had been seized by a white-hot rage when she admitted she was Connie's sister, so much so that he'd had to struggle to control it. The session in the squash courts today was proof of it. It had built inside him like a whip, licking at him relentlessly. He had been lethal on the courts today. Nobody had been able to touch him. But at least it was an outlet, and an acceptable one, for what he felt. But the anger hadn't gone; it was still seething inside him. He wasn't sure what he was going to do about it.

He stripped off his clothes and stepped into the shower. The cool water hit his skin, and he closed his eyes and let it rush over his muscled shoulders and powerful frame. One thing he knew. He had to stay away from Laura until he sorted out in his mind exactly how he felt, and he knew he wasn't at all sure what he did feel. To his continuing amazement, he still thought about her all the time, and there were still other powerful emotions mixed in with the anger that he seemed to have no control over. His body ached when he thought of the weekend on the yacht. His powerful body surged at the thought, and he slammed his hand against the shower wall. Tonight he would get drunk, really tie one on. And then he would find himself a woman—any woman—and stop driving himself crazy.

Chapter 8

On Monday Laura returned to work. Only three days had passed since Connie had walked back into her life, but to Laura those three days seemed like an eternity. When she reached her desk, her gaze swept furtively toward the hangar, but she could see Quint nowhere. She knew that all day long she would be looking for him and that sooner or later she would see him. It would only be a matter of time. And she wondered what he would do? Would he even acknowledge her presence? Or would he pretend she didn't exist?

She went to work and didn't look up again until it was lunchtime. Sliding out from behind her desk, she walked slowly to the canteen. Again there was no sign of Quint. She ate her lunch with a sinking feeling and returned to her desk. In the afternoon she stopped for coffee at the machine, but saw nothing of him. She concluded that he was making a deliberate effort not to bump into her, probably going out to eat at a nearby fast-food restaurant, skipping his coffee breaks. The death knell sounded for their relationship, as if she needed any further proof.

That came on Wednesday.

She saw Quint walk into Mr. Barnes's office, and all her senses leaped at the sight of him, but he kept his back to her. Her gaze bored into his broad shoulders, willing him in vain to turn around. She knew that he knew she was watching. His rigid stance shouted a silent message across the space of the office. As far as he was concerned, she no longer existed, that was perfectly clear. She swallowed hard, fighting back the sting of tears. Nor did he even angle his head sideways so she could catch a glimpse of his profile, so there was no chance whatsoever that his gaze might stray her way. The silent monolithic message said it all. She watched him with hungry eyes, drinking him in like some thirsting traveler having at last spotted water.

The familiar shape of him, the angle of his head, the hands that had touched her so intimately, the images that flashed through her mind of his body covering hers, twisting with hers in a tangled maze in the heat of passion brought a flush to her face and a deep ache that needed to be filled. She longed to be with him again, simply to feel the way he made her feel in his presence, to experience the fun they had together and, above all else, to feel his mouth covering hers and his arms tightening around her with that quick response as desire raced between them. Now all that was gone. Irretrievably lost. She lowered her gaze and tried to quell the terrible sense of loss and to blink back the sting of encroaching tears.

She looked up again to see that he was getting ready to leave Mr. Barnes's office. He walked out the door into the hangar without so much as a glance in her direction, yet she sensed that every sensitive nerve ending in his body was tuned to hers, as hers were to his. She went back to her work, telling herself that it had been bound to turn out this way. She knew that sooner or later, somehow, someway, he would have discovered the truth. Connie's arrival had only speeded things up. Look upon it as a favor, Laura told herself. If it had happened later, she would have only been that much more deeply in love with him, things would only have been that much harder. The thought didn't comfort her very much because she couldn't imagine being any more in love with him than she already was.

Jim Barnes glanced her way with a perplexed expression on his face, so she bent her head industriously and put her mind back on her work, chiding herself for being submerged in her personal problems during work hours.

Later that day, Mr. Barnes called her in.

"Sit down, Laura," he said, gesturing toward a chair. "I want to have a word with you."

She did as he asked and began to feel uneasy.

He cleared his throat. "I don't usually pry into my employees' private lives, but I can tell you that I'm going to make an exception this time because it involves two people that I think very highly of. Two employees whom I would hate to lose."

He rose from the desk and walked around to where she sat. Leaning on the desk, he kept his voice low so that no one could possibly overhear. In spite of the fact that the office was glassed in and the door closed, that he took this added precaution underlined the seriousness of what he was about to say.

"I've heard via the grapevine that you've been seeing Quint Jones, Laura. Now, I don't know what's wrong. That's none of my business. I only know that something is affecting Quint deeply. He's practically undergone a personality change. While there has been no call for complaint, I can see a change in you, too. You're not the same cheerful person, and Quint is like a bear with a thorn in his paw. He's been mean as hell to deal with for the past week. I had to speak to him this morning about it, and he informed me that he's thinking of leaving. I couldn't pry any reason out of him, only a promise that he would think it over for another week before he did anything about it.

"I don't want to lose an excellent pilot. They're too hard to come by. So I'm butting in, Laura, to ask if there's anything I can do?"

She shook her head and rose quietly. Mr. Barnes's words had set off alarm bells inside her head. Quint couldn't afford to leave this job; he might not find another one. Especially one that he was trained for and one that he enjoyed doing. She would leave Cranston's before she would see Quint quit his job. It was so important to him. The knowledge that he was having trouble cut her to the quick.

"I'm sorry, Mr. Barnes, that ... the trouble between Quint and me has had such a negative effect on his behavior and that he's thinking of leaving his job.

I appreciate your telling me. I'll talk to him as soon as possible and try to smooth things over the best I can,'' she murmured. If that was even possible, her mind shouted silently, if he would even listen. But she knew she had to try.

Jim had three daughters and was well versed in the full range of feminine behavior. Hers at the moment was a dead giveaway.

''He hasn't done anything wrong, Laura. His flying, his work, are all impeccable. I want to put your mind at rest on that score.''

Laura gazed steadily into Jim Barnes's kindly eyes. It was as if he were rooting for the two of them, not simply because he was ensuring that he didn't lose a good employee, but because he wanted to see the two of them work things out. It made her even more fond of him than she already was.

''It's just been hell trying to get along with him. He's been snapping everyone's heads off. That is when he bothers to answer anyone at all.'' He smiled wryly. ''I'm sure that as soon as you two sort out whatever's wrong between you, he'll get back to normal, and so will you.''

She smiled back at him. ''Thank you, Mr. Barnes.''

''Good luck.''

As she left, she wondered how on earth she was going to get Quint to talk to her when he wouldn't even look her way.

She sat back down at her desk and went back to her work, on a kind of automatic pilot, leaving a part of her mind free to figure out some way to talk to him. When she was finished with the time schedule, she pulled Quint's application from the files and made a note of his home address.

She left work with the hastily scribbled address stuck in her handbag, and instead of going to her own apartment, drove toward his home.

She knew that if she telephoned, he would probably put down the receiver. She knew from experience that it was futile to try to discuss something as serious as this on the phone. It was always better to talk face-to-face. If Quint didn't accept or like what she had to say, he couldn't hang up on her; once she was there, he would have to hear her out.

She drove swiftly toward Cherry Street, and finally, after some searching, found a block of condominiums facing the river. They were expensive-looking, and the neighborhood was well kept. She walked up to the door, marshalling her thoughts and trying to compose herself. She knocked and rang the bell, but there was no answer. The silence was an anticlimax. She sighed, regretting having worked herself up to fever pitch only to discover he wasn't even there. She turned and started to walk down the pathway, trying to think of what to do next, when she saw a black Jaguar slow down, swing into the driveway at a fast clip and then screech to a halt.

It was Quint. Laura's heart began to beat with a heavy thud, and every nerve in her body danced in tune to his presence.

He slid out of the car like a lazy jungle cat, slammed the car door with an emphatic bang and stood leaning indolently against the side of the Jaguar, surveying her with hard, calculating, insolent eyes. Eyes that said, what the hell are you doing here?

She felt all her resolve draining away and began to tremble imperceptibly under this silent, hostile perusal. She struggled to remain clam, to remember what she wanted to say to him, but she knew she was fighting a losing battle. Still, she had to try.

"Quint, I have to talk to you. We have to talk," she repeated, and stepped forward.

He moved away from the car and stood towering over her, staring at her enigmatically, saying nothing, weighing, measuring. A chill ran down her spine. He was not in a receptive mood, but it looked as though he was going to let her in and listen out of sheer curiosity. All other emotions were carefully screened and controlled behind his stare.

He led the way to the front entrance of his condo and opened it with a deft flick of the key. Once inside, he gestured toward a large, airy room that had sliding doors and a patio facing the river.

Laura walked into the center of the room and stood watching him as he closed the door behind him, her gaze trailing over the casual slacks that outlined the long, lean line of his legs and narrow hips and the casual shirt that clung to his broad shoulders.

Then he turned.

"How are things, Cathy?" he said with a flick of cynical derision, giving emphasis to her old name. "How are you going to lie your way out of this one?" He opened the top buttons of his shirt and crossed the room.

"I want to explain a few things about what happened all those years ago," she started hesitantly.

"Well, that's good. Because I would like to hear a few explanations about why you and your sister stole several of the best years out of my life," he fired back. The words shot across the room like bullets with strong emotion propelling them. Quint stood with his hands planted firmly on his narrow hips, challenging, daring her to explain it away. "Not only stole those years, but ruined my reputation and tainted the rest of my life."

She'd known this was going to be hard. She had expected no less, but somehow now, with those gray, calculating eyes boring into her and the planes and angles of his face set into a harsh mask, whatever she had to say seemed laughable. There were no simple explanations. But there were reasons and circumstances.

"I'm not trying to make any excuses," she murmured softly. "No one can ever make up to you for what happened. What was done was entirely wrong. All I can do is to try to explain the circumstances that led up to it."

His features seemed set in stone, but he allowed her to continue.

Her words seemed hopelessly inadequate, but she forced herself to go on. "To give you some insight into why my sister... and I... did what we did."

"I'm all ears. I always wanted to know why people lie and ruin other people's lives to save their own necks. Come on out with it." His gray eyes stung hers with cruel mockery.

She started to speak, but her voice faltered. The words seemed to stick in her throat. She loved him, and the expression on his face was so implacable and contemptuous that she knew in that instant whatever feeling she had hoped he still had for her was gone, lost forever. It was this painful realization that made her stumble over her words, indeed, made it difficult to get the words out at all. If anything, the features of his handsome face grew more derisive at her halting attempts at speech.

"Don't stop now, Laura. We both know how good you are at giving performances. Not just good, totally convincing, in fact," he purred with smooth menace. "You had me completely fooled until I saw that sister of yours in the car next to you. And, of course, there was a jury of twelve people that you won over. Let's not forget that."

She blanched at his words.

"Let's see if you can do it again," he added with a quiet challenge.

Fighting for control, she started again. "It was my stepfather, Les. We were both terrified of him," she blurted out raggedly. "The whole household revolved around his moods. We tiptoed around him, groveled around him, were careful not to even move or breathe when he was in one of his violent moods. It went on for years. And inevitably, it took its toll on both our personalities. But in completely different ways. It made Connie wild and restless, and she did crazy things. She went running around with a fast crowd, going out with all sorts of guys. Going to wild parties—driving too fast," she added pointedly. "But it had a completely different effect on me. It made me withdraw." She gazed at Quint steadily.

"It also made you into a damned good liar," he said sharply. "Let's not forget that. God, you had me fooled." He pulled out a cigarette from a box on the table and lit it with a silver lighter. He studied her through the smoke with indifferent eyes and waited for whatever was coming next.

"I was *terrified* of him and his moods. You must believe that. If we didn't do what he wanted, he went wild, and he was capable of almost anything." Her voice was low and the words faded. "One day he…he tried to, to rape me." In torment, she looked up at Quint's face, a rigid impassive mask that gave nothing away. She forced herself to continue. "Connie burst into the house and saved me. We both knew he would try again." She couldn't meet Quint's eyes. He was the first person she'd ever told. Fear and humiliation swept her.

"When Connie crashed the car and hit that old man, she knew instantly that she would have to go to prison. She also knew that if she went to prison, it would mean leaving me alone with Les. I was a minor," she whispered desperately. "I had nowhere to go. Connie panicked when she realized that not only would she have to face going to prison but she would have to leave me to him. He would have used me Quint, abused me physically and mentally. So Connie somehow got you behind the wheel of that car. When the police came and you were still out, she told them you'd been driving. She made me promise to lie to cover up. She filled me with terror. She said that if she wasn't around, if *she* went to jail and not you, that I would be Les's sexual toy. I knew she wasn't lying. I knew it was true," Laura gasped. "I knew he was capable of almost anything." Her trembling voice indicated the depth of emotion she felt when she thought of her stepfather, even after all this time. "I was only sixteen," she added. "I couldn't face that. I was nearly rigid with fear, and I couldn't think straight.'' She lowered her head and tried to force back the tears that the memory brought on. She blinked rapidly before she resumed.

All was silent. You could hear a pin drop in the heavy silence, Laura thought. Quint's eyes were still cold and hostile, but he was listening with rapt attention. She hurried on.

"I can never make up to you for what happened. I wish I could. But sometimes if people know why somebody did something awful to them, it makes it easier to bear, maybe, even in time, enables them to forgive.'' The look in his eyes didn't waver or give away anything of what he was thinking.

"I never wanted to fall in love with you," she went on softly. "The last thing I ever wanted was for something to happen between us. I never wanted to go out with you. I never wanted you to even notice me. That was why I avoided you or disappeared every time you came near. But it was a mistake. All it did was achieve the opposite effect. You became interested or offended or both. You reproached me, and when you did, I had such an awful conscience about what I had done, about how I made you feel like an outcast from society, that when you more or less challenged me to go out with you, to prove to you that it wasn't the stigma of your background that was driving me away, I had to prove it to you. And that was all I intended to do, to prove to you that I wasn't avoiding you for that reason. I felt I owed you a great deal and that that was the least I could do. So I went out with you. I never dreamed that what happened would happen.

"I found myself strongly attracted to you, more strongly attracted than to any man I had ever met. And I seemed to have less and less control over my feelings. I tried to avoid you again because I could see what was happening, but you came after me, and from then on I didn't seem to have much say in the matter. You took over, and I found myself falling in love with you."

He had been silent the whole time, listening to her without interrupting, without a flicker of emotion in his eyes. He turned calmly and crushed the cigarette out on the nearest ashtray, then looked at her steadily. There was a wry twist to his mouth.

"That was very good, Laura. It really was. You're a very convincing actress. In fact, I think you missed your calling. You should be on the stage," he murmured with soft menace, and strode forward. "And you know what else? You're beautiful, too, and that adds to it," he said huskily. "That's what makes you all the more dangerous. That's what makes that tortured look in those gorgeous green eyes all the more convincing somehow," he added as he stood towering over her for a long moment before he went on.

"Do you know why you haven't heard from me? Why I never demanded an explanation when you told me you were Connie's sister? It was because I didn't trust myself. I was afraid of what I might do." His hands tightened on her arms so hard that she winced slightly.

"I was afraid I might wring that beautiful neck of yours. I thought I might do almost anything. I had to stay away from you just to calm down and think. And I have been thinking, Laura."

She stood silently fighting back the tears induced by his words, gazing unwaveringly back at him as she realized that her confession had had little effect, if any.

"Do you have any idea of what it's like to be locked up, to have your freedom taken away?" he demanded, the line of his sensual mouth thinned.

She shook her head, unable to speak.

"No. You don't. No one does who has never experienced the unspeakable horror of it. You can't even imagine what it's like. You can't begin to realize or appreciate the endless hours ticking away. You can't imagine the kinds of people there are inside those places, nor can you begin to imagine the sheer hell of knowing you're paying a price for something you didn't even do. And that's only the half of it." His hands tightened, and he shook her slightly to emphasize his final words. "When you come out, there's the trick of trying to fit back into the world. Have you any idea of what that's like?"

She shook her head again as tears began to roll down her face.

"No, you don't," he said softly. "You can't even begin to imagine what that's like or what it's like to be treated like a leper by people who formerly liked and respected you, who turn their backs on you and pretend they didn't even see you.

"Damn your sister," he said hoarsely between gritted teeth. "I hope she rots in hell. She was the main cause of it all. I hate her, pure and simple, no problem there." He paused. "But you. You're another story altogether." His face grew dark with the havoc warring inside him.

"You stir up all kinds of mixed emotions inside me that I can't sort out. And it's slowly driving me crazy trying to do it. I fell in love with you," he whispered huskily, "hook line and sinker. And I made love to you. It was something I can't forget. I remember what it was like to have you in my arms, to feel you underneath me, to be inside you."

Laura began to tremble at his words and at the raw desire that stirred inside both of them.

"What's more, I want to be there again," he murmured. "I want you right now, right here, right this minute. And I hate myself for wanting you." He ground out the words. "Because, at the same time, I keep remembering what your damned sister and you did to me, and I haven't been able to forgive you for that. It's driving me crazy, feeling this way." He shook her again, then let her go and walked away to the other side of the room.

She stood staring after him.

"I'm sorry," Laura whispered brokenly. "I'm so sorry." The words sounded inane, they were so inadequate, but there was little else she could think of to say.

"That doesn't do me much good." He laughed scornfully, giving her the full impact of his stormy, gray eyes. "You have to do better than come up with an 'I'm sorry.'"

"I wish there was a way I could make it up to you," she added helplessly.

"There is a way, Laura. Believe me there is." His gray eyes flicked over her insolently.

"You can marry me."

Laura's eyes widened, and she and Quint stared silently at each other for several long moments. Laura couldn't answer at first, she was so stunned by his words. Then a protest exploded from her.

"You're mad! You can't mean it! That wouldn't be a marriage, it would be a sham, a parody of a marriage and all that marriage should stand for."

"Do you want to make it up to me?" he asked, his face stony. "You said you wished there was a way you could make it up to me. I'm giving you one, and it's not as crazy as it first sounds. Think about it for a minute or two," he drawled. "You're the perfect wife for me, Laura," he went on, his voice laced with wry innuendo. "I have nothing to hide from you. You know all about me. We get along well together. And because I'm one of the world's biggest fools," he added with sarcastic derision aimed at himself, "I still want you like hell, honey. Let me be clear. I hate you for what you did, and I'd like to make you pay, but that doesn't stop me from wanting you."

He walked slowly toward her. She did want to make it up to him, but the far stronger emotion inside her was that she loved him with all her heart. She was swayed powerfully by it, every inch of her still desiring him. At the same time, she wondered how life would be, married to him when a part of him despised her. But as her eyes slid over the familiar lines of his face, the gray eyes that locked with hers, the high cheekbones, tapering male jaw and the sensual mouth, she knew she wanted him in spite of everything. And as he put his hands on her again, desire surged up inside her, just as potently as it had always done.

"I paid a debt to society that I never owed," he murmured huskily as he bent his head and brushed the side of her face with his lips. The words trickled into her ear. "And now you have a debt to pay to me." His hands slid into her hair, around the back of her neck, and he pulled her to him roughly and lowered his head to kiss her. His stormy, gray eyes probed hers before his warm mobile mouth covered hers. A muffled protest stayed locked in her throat as he took what he wanted, kissing her with almost bruising intensity as his hands left her hair and moved down her back, then along her hips, pressing her into him with a hot, hungry, yet angry need. He grabbed a handful of her skirt and slid his hand underneath and cupped her rounded bottom in a crude display of his possession.

Laura started to struggle in protest, but his hands instantly tightened their grip, grinding her into him until a powerful surge of desire eddied deep inside her and her mouth parted underneath his. He felt her response instantly, and his kisses, though still insistent and demanding, eased and the old magic began to rush between them, surging like a breaker rising in the surf, firing them both with its instant hot need. Soon her hands wrapped around his neck, and her body arched into his as she kissed him back with wild abandon. Then abruptly he removed her arms from around his neck and held her away from him. His narrowed gaze bored into her. The ragged edge to his breathing testified to his grudging but swift arousal.

"It's pretty obvious that I want you. But I also want an answer, and I want it now. No more delays."

She still loved him, nothing had changed that. Not this hard veneer that covered his feelings nor this deep anger she felt emanating from him in an almost palpable force. Not only did she still love him, but she still wanted him and couldn't imagine surviving in the arid desert life would become without him. She wanted him under any conditions, under whatever terms he dictated.

"Yes. I'll marry you," she said breathlessly.

Something seemed to relax inside him, but it was soon hidden, and the hard shell and the closed taut expression in his face remained.

"We'll get married as soon as possible. It's settled."

There was finality to his words, she noted. There was no backing out now.

Chapter 9

The wedding was held in the small chapel of a much larger church. Laura wore a white silk organza off-the-shoulder gown. Her hair was swept up. A small crown of flowers was intertwined in the curls and small wisps surrounded and framed the delicate contours of her face. Tina was her lady of honor, and Jim Barnes was best man for Quint. The chapel was crammed with people from Cranston's. The announcement of the wedding had been a popular one with the other employees. Afterward, there was a small reception and dinner held at an Italian restaurant. A lively band accompanied the wedding dinner, playing a soft medley of music.

The bride and groom were toasted. Laura gazed up at her husband, who was dressed in a gray suit with matching waistcoat, crisp white shirt and pearl-gray silk tie with a thin black stripe. His dark hair was well groomed, his gray eyes flinty, the deep tan of his skin contrasting strikingly with the impeccable conservative lines of his suit. He was that rare mixture of tough manliness and smooth edges, and Laura's admiring gaze slid over him from time to time as she chatted amiably with the wedding guests. She wondered if they noticed the impenetrable look in his cool gray eyes, the manufactured smile he put on during the wedding dinner. If anyone did, it wasn't mentioned. There were only wistful straying glances of admiration from the women and the occasional good-natured banter from the men aimed in Quint's direction.

Laura wondered if she would ever again see the warmth and sunny glint that she missed in his eyes. Ever since she'd said she would marry him, he seemed to have put on emotional armor, as if he had to protect himself from allowing her to get too close. Nothing she could do or say had any effect.

As a bride and groom, Laura and Quint were exceedingly attractive. When he asked her to dance and she rose and smiled, there was a spontaneous burst of applause.

"We're expected to lead off the dancing," he explained, giving her one of his public smiles.

She realized it was not something he was doing to celebrate their marriage, but that he was simply going through the motions, doing what was expected of them. She took his hand, and he swept her onto the small dance floor. Everybody was watching.

He smiled down at her, and they appeared to be a blissfully happy couple. Only Laura could see the look in his eyes, the hard, unforgiving flare when his gaze flickered over her. The band broke into a romantic rendition of a barcarole, and they waltzed around the floor.

"Smile," he said. "You look like you're scheduled for the guillotine."

"What do I have to smile about?" she murmured. "*You* look as though you want to eat me alive."

"Part of me does. The other part of me wants something quite different."

She flushed, and the color creeping up her bare shoulders and neck and finally her face made the corners of his mouth pull into the nearest thing to a genuine smile she had seen all day.

"You really are a consummate actress. How you can blush, Laura, beats me." He grinned with sardonic derision and whirled her around.

She smiled back at him fixedly, for the benefit of those watching, but there was a wounded glint in her eyes, as a sense of despair grew inside her.

At last the wedding dinner ended and the guests and the bride and groom made for parked cars. Confetti and rice were hurled in a shower as Quint and Laura climbed into Quint's car, which was festooned with ribbons and tin cans. Laura kissed Tina and Mr. Barnes, thanked them and then waved goodbye. She tossed her bouquet of white lilies to Tina, who caught it with a shout of delight.

Loud cries of farewell and a few ribald remarks from some of the men followed them as they drove away. Laura leaned back with a sigh of relief, brushing off confetti and rice from her arms and neck and the skirt of her gown, glad that it was over, forgetting for the moment the grim man sitting next to her.

She looked over at her husband and then down at the ring on her finger. She was married. The total realization of what she had done was finally making itself felt.

Quint must have sensed her sudden dismay because his head turned and there was a wry twist to his mouth.

"It's too late to change your mind, Mrs. Jones. You can't lie your way out of this one."

The remark stung her as did all his quiet little barbs, and she turned away to look out the window, hoping that this need to strike back at her would diminish as soon as they were settled into married life. She told herself fervently that it would be so and clung to it as a drowning man clings to a raft in a turbulent sea. Silence hung heavily between them. Laura couldn't think of anything to say; he had killed stone dead the desire to make conversation.

"Do you have everything you need?" he finally asked.

"Yes," she murmured, thinking she had everything but his love.

"We can stop by your apartment tomorrow and pick up the rest of your things."

"Fine," she murmured coolly, still not looking at him. She sensed a surge of sudden irritation in him, but he said nothing and drove swiftly through the streets until they reached his condo, where he helped her as she lifted the yards of organza. He walked ahead and unlocked the door. Then without warning he suddenly swept her up in his arms and carried her across the threshold. She was so stunned that all she could do was gasp.

"It's bad luck not to carry the bride over the threshold," he said, as if that had been the only reason for the sentimental and romantic gesture. His gaze locked with hers as he moved through the doorway with her in his arms. Once inside, he put her down and immediately began to loosen his tie impatiently.

"I'm going to get out of these clothes." With a suitcase in each hand, he strode up the stairs that led to the bedroom level of the condo. Laura lifted the long skirt of the bridal gown and followed.

"Do you want to fly down to the Keys or go somewhere else?" he called over his shoulder. They had discussed it briefly before the wedding but had not come up with anything definite in the way of plans. They had only a few days before they had to return to work.

"Let's go back to the Keys," she said. "We enjoyed ourselves there so much last time."

"All right," he agreed, his face still an expressionless mask as he led the way into the master bedroom and put down their suitcases. He started unfastening the stiff collar of his shirt and soon unlooped his tie, tore it from around his neck and flung it onto a nearby chair, along with his jacket. He stood gazing steadily at her as he unbuttoned his waistcoat and then his shirt.

In the hectic rush before the wedding, they had spent little time together. What time there was had been used to discuss the arrangements for the wedding. Quint had kept his physical needs simmering on a back burner. Now there was no need for restraint. Laura heard him moving up behind her to help her with the long zipper down the back of her bridal gown. She felt unaccountably nervous. She had not experienced any edginess with him the first time they had made love, but her feelings had been different then, as had his whole attitude.

"I'll just get out of these things and into something...are we going to fly down tonight?" she asked, turning around.

"I think it's a bit late for that, don't you," he noted, a gleam beginning to dance in his eyes. He stripped off his shirt, his eyes sliding languorously over her.

She gazed back at him for a brief moment as heat began coursing through her veins. "I'll just get out of this," she murmured, and began to take the frothy gown off, peeling it from her shoulders and then stepping out of it and laying it neatly across the chair. She heard him move closer to her. She held her breath as he stood barely an inch behind her. She didn't dare breathe, she didn't dare speak, and then he reached out and pulled her back against the lean hard length of him. And began kissing her, his mouth closing over hers, his hands caressing her.

"Do you want to get into the bathroom first, or shall I?" She panicked and pulled away from him. Suddenly embarrassed, she excused herself, not wanting to undress in front of him any further. With a cold, enigmatic stare, he retreated.

Inside the bathroom, Laura stripped off the long flounced slip that was worn underneath the gown. Panties and bra quickly followed before she stepped inside the shower cubicle. When she came out, she pulled on a robe that hung on the door and began to brush her hair in long, soothing strokes, trying to ease the tension that was building inside her. What was wrong with her? This was the man she loved; nothing had changed that. Why was she acting like a nervous virgin? She surveyed her face in the bevel-edged mirror, an apprehensive look in her eyes. It was Quint. He was so different from the man who had made love to her on the yacht. He was distant, a man hiding his very soul from her, a man with a protective armor surrounding him, a man capable of discharging stinging darts whenever she came too close.

Golden-brown curls released from the upswept hairstyle cascaded around her face. She brushed her teeth and stalled for time, not wanting to go out into the bedroom, suddenly afraid of the cold glint in Quint's eyes, afraid of what lay behind it and what it would mean when she was in his arms. He wouldn't make love with the warm passion she had known with the smiling Quint of before. She removed her make-up, cleansed her skin and then brushed her hair again.

Suddenly the door sprang open. Laura's gaze locked with Quint's in the mirror.

"I was just finishing," she murmured.

He lounged in the doorway, his naked torso drawing her eyes like a magnet. He was barefoot and wore only his suit pants. His lean masculinity held a sensual impact.

"You wouldn't be hiding from me, Laura, would you?" he challenged.

"No," she said, with a surge of defiance. "I was just finishing. I was coming out to get a nightgown."

"I don't think you'll need it," he asserted, his gray eyes darkening.

His words caused a heat rush to surge through her. She shuddered and started to brush past him quickly.

"I always sleep in a nightgown," she retorted.

"Not in my bed."

"It's not..." Laura began softly. But her words were halted as his hand pulled her through the doorway and into the bedroom as if she were a shy schoolgirl.

Once inside the room, lit only by a table lamp, he impelled her toward him. He untied the sash of her robe so that it fell open. His arms slid inside and around her back, pulling her up against the lean, hard wall of his bare torso. She gasped, and his head bent, and his mouth covered hers in a hungry, demanding kiss, a punishing kiss that bruised and chastened and demanded and excited. For a brief moment, she went rigid, pushing against him. Her reaction only made him more determined and his kisses more insistent.

Quint groaned softly in Laura's ear, and the sensual magic of his masculinity began to penetrate her entire being. Then her stiffness melted as he began to kiss her with that rhythmic, demanding need that set her blood on her fire. His hands slid over the smooth skin of her back and hips, grasping her to him as the repressed need of the weeks leading up to the wedding made itself felt and surged between them. Her arms soon locked around his neck, and her body bowed to his. Their legs intertwined as they moved restlessly to get nearer to each other, to defy the limitations of their own bodies.

Quint broke off the succession of kisses and pulled back slightly, his eyes narrowed with aroused desire.

"Let me look at you," Quint said in that low-pitched, rusty voice that signaled his aroused state. He slid the robe from her shoulders.

Laura closed her eyes briefly and then opened them, watching his gaze scorch her skin with its fiery trail. With trembling hands he drew her to him, and they rolled onto the bed, his mouth finding hers instantly. Laura responded, letting the desire intoxicate her like a heady wine, before he broke off the kiss.

There were no words between them, she noted dimly as she felt the rush of desire overtaking her. No incoherent words were whispered this time while passion built. Caught up in the whirlwind of his need and hers, Laura realized vaguely, there was excitement, but there was no tenderness. But her need for him was so great that it didn't matter, and all else faded as his knee nudged her thighs apart and his head lowered to tease one sensitive nipple, filling her with an empty ache to have him deep inside her.

He thrust into her gently, then with a fiery hunger, and Laura felt that black chasm of sensation opening up and swallowing her as desire overwhelmed them and drove them to a rising crescendo of pleasure. Quint's body drove into hers with a seemingly insatiable hunger, as if the very feel of her were driving him crazy. The spiraling pleasure spun out of control. As they reached that final peak, Quint's choked responses seemed torn from him, and Laura gasped at the final surge of exquisite sensation, clenching his broad-muscled shoulders. Then they lay back, gasping from the stunning, indescribable satisfaction, floating down into a valley of sublime peace.

Laura felt Quint's hands clasp and unclasp as he buried his face in the side of her neck. His harsh breathing filled her ears, testifying to the pitch of excitement his body and mind had reached. She was stunned once again by the response he triggered from her, feeling as though she had just come once again out of a dark, churning place of sensation. Silent minutes ticked away, punctuated only by the subsidence of their breathing. Laura waited for some murmur of an endearment, a tender kiss, even a gentle whisper of her name. But Quint simply rolled away.

A few minutes later, she heard him get up and go into the shower. With a sense of overwhelming defeat, she realized that he was determined to keep warm emotions out of their marriage altogether. She was here simply to satisfy his physical needs. Whatever tender feelings he had were locked away, buried deep inside him. His physical needs were going to be satisfied, and hers, but he was withholding all other emotions. She blinked rapidly as tears stung the backs of her eyes.

She heard the shower pelting the tiles and running down the drain. Slowly she slid from the side of the bed and looked at the clock. From her suitcase, she pulled the white lace-and-satin nightgown she hadn't had time to put on. She let it slither over her head, and then she picked up her bathrobe and fastened the tie around her waist. She walked over to his dresser and picked up a hairbrush and began to run it through her softly curling mane of hair. Her eyes glistened, their expression softened by the ravages of their lovemaking, her lips slightly rosy from his demanding kisses. When she heard the bathroom door open, she whirled around. His gray eyes slid over her hungrily, the banked fire still flickering.

"Would you like a snack? Did you have enough to eat at the reception?" she asked. It was quite a few hours since the wedding dinner.

"I'm not hungry," he said, advancing toward her. As he drew near, his hands began undoing the sash of her robe. She moved to knock his hands away.

"What's the matter?" He laughed softly and enveloped her against his leanly muscled length.

"You know what's wrong," she cried softly. "This isn't the way it was before."

"Things are not the same as they were before. Damn it. You know that, and I know that," he reminded her coldly. "I told you how I felt before we got married." She pushed with her hands against his bare shoulders. He had only a towel wrapped around him.

"You know you want me. Just as much as I want you," he said, nuzzling her ear.

"No," she started to protest, but his head ducked, and his mouth caught hers. His hands parted her robe and slid inside. Laura felt herself engulfed once again in a dark chasm of desire with the bottom falling dizzily away.

They flew down to Key West and cruised on the same yacht that they had been on together before. Laura's heart swelled with happiness when they reached it, as she remembered the glorious two days they had spent on it. By midafternoon they had dropped anchor near the reef where they had gone snorkeling before.

Laura had changed into her swimsuit and had twisted her hair on top of her head. She stretched in the saturating blaze of the sun, longing to get into the aquamarine water for a swim after the hours of traveling. The horizon was cloudless, and the endless gulf waters and sky that surrounded them were soaked in the brightness of the sun. She looked down at her bare feet and tapering brown legs and thought how wonderful it was to be back. Then she glanced pensively at the gold band on her finger.

She saw Quint lope toward the cockpit, his lean, broad-shouldered muscularity outlined by the endless sea and sky around him. Laura's face flushed when she remembered his hands on her body, and she turned away and removed her wedding ring, thinking it might somehow slip off and be lost in the water. She wondered, as she picked up her mask and flippers, how long Quint was going to maintain this cool distance. Being with him was like being with a distant, polite stranger. The only time he discarded this attitude was in bed. Then a fiery need of passion consumed them both. Surely in time...

"Come on, are you ready?" he asked. She heard the splash of the dinghy in the water and moved to the swimming ladder and descended with her mask and flippers in her hand. They rowed to the reef and left the dinghy bobbing on the surface as they plunged into the clear water.

The time sped by. They explored historic Key West one morning and then cruised around the keys surrounding it, anchoring when it suited them. They swam and explored the reefs and, afterward, sprawled on the decks exhausted, dozing briefly in the tiny pools of water streaming off their bodies. In the late afternoon they went below, put tapes in the tape deck and prepared some dinner. Quint moved around the gal-

ley fixing cool, tempting drinks into which he tossed
several different kinds of fruit juice and wine and
slices of lime. Laura prepared salad, fish and sliced
rolls, thinking all the time that they were in an ideal
setting, romantic and isolated from the humdrum
world of everyday life. It should have been heaven, but
it was just a parody of a honeymoon, since the main
ingredient—namely, love—seemed to be missing.
Laura swallowed hard trying to suppress the empty
ache that the thought produced inside her.

The hours trickled away one by one, and neither the
sunshine nor the sparkling tropical waters had any effect on Quint's disposition. He held himself away, self-
contained, aloof, apart. He constantly seemed to be
around but never close. Laura began to seethe silently
at this infuriating treatment, and by the second day
she threw her mask on the teak deck and turned to
confront him.

"I hope we will be going back today," she announced as she pulled an elastic out of her hair so that
it cascaded to her shoulders.

With a sardonic twist to his mouth, Quint turned to
look at her. "What's the matter, Laura?"

"Why stay any longer?" she muttered. "This is a
disaster. You've been determined to wreck it."

"If that's how you feel, let's go," he replied with an
impassive expression on his face.

His indifference and ready acceptance to concede
that the honeymoon was a disaster were even more irritating than the way he'd been behaving. She stalked
from the deck and went below to the master bunk,
stripped off her wet swimsuit, put on shorts and a T-
shirt and pushed her feet into sandals.

She heard him enter the bunk and whirled around. "Why didn't you tell me? You didn't want to come away. We could have stayed at the condo," she cried softly. "Instead of coming on this...this fiasco." There were tears of anger in her eyes. But she saw the corners of his mouth curl with a kind of grim satisfaction.

"I've done no such thing," he ground out. "If anyone's ruined anything, if we want to place the blame for this *fiasco*, we could lay it at your door, not mine. Besides, it hasn't been a complete fiasco. There's been one thing about it that's been good," he said huskily. "And we both know what that is. Nothing seems to dampen our desire for each other, not lies or deceptions or prison records or ruined chances."

Laura looked down at her hands, defeated.

Later that afternoon they finished their packing, and Quint went back up on deck to bring up the anchor so that they could begin making their way back toward the marina.

The flight home was quiet, barely a word was spoken between them, and when they reached the condo, the atmosphere remained the same. Laura reflected that she'd been foolish to have hoped that things would have ironed themselves out by the end of their trip. It was obviously going to take a lot longer than that. She sighed and ran a distracted hand through her hair and told herself to hang on. He would lose his negative feelings in time; she simply had to be more patient. Living together, sharing the ups and downs of everyday life would bring them together, she convinced herself. The love that he had shown her before, surely it was still there; it was simply inaccessible for the time being. The physical need that he had for her meant something. It wasn't just lust. If that had been the case, he could have satisfied a purely physical need with almost anyone without going to the trouble of getting himself entangled in a marriage. Quint had married *her*, and that counted for something. Laura clung to these remnants of hope and told herself that, in time, things would be different, he would gradually let down those barriers he had built around himself. She was sure of it. One didn't have to be an expert on love to know one thing—that love is one of the strongest emotions there is. Stronger than anything else, in fact—a ruling passion. And in time it would win out over those others holding sway at the moment. The thought brightened her mood, and she walked around the condo with a lighter step.

On Monday they returned to Cranston's. Laura was glad to have the day filled once again with her work and for Quint to be absorbed by his. It left less time for her to contemplate their present state of affairs, to brood about what was missing from their lives. In the evening she came home and prepared dinner, thinking it would be their first real meal together in their home.

Quint walked in and went straight into the shower. Laura kept the casserole warm in the oven. When she stepped out into the hall to ask Quint if he'd want any dessert, to her dismay she saw him striding out the door. Frantically she ran after him.

"Where are you going?" she cried into the heavy summer night.

"Out," his voice returned with a lazy flatness, and he got into the car and slammed the door.

Laura released a small wounded gasp, and a defeated look eddied into her eyes as she watched him drive away. She walked back to the kitchen and stared at the dinner. Finally she filled a plate with some of the hot, bubbling casserole, pulled a tossed green salad from the refrigerator and sat down and began to eat the food she had so carefully prepared, feeling as though Quint was punishing her. What could she expect? After what she'd done to him, did she really think a nicely cooked dinner, a few kind deeds were going to put it right? She almost laughed at her naiveté. It was glaringly clear that this was going to be a long, hard haul, and that Quint was calling all the shots.

She dropped her fork onto her plate. The sound shattered the silence of the kitchen and jarred her nerves. She crossed the kitchen to get a glass of milk and stood drinking it pensively, wondering where on earth Quint had gone. She really didn't want to think about where he was, she suddenly realized uncomfortably.

After cleaning the kitchen, she read for a while, then, feeling drowsy, she went upstairs to bed. She didn't hear Quint when he came home.

In the morning at breakfast, she watched Quint over the rim of her coffee cup as he read the paper. He had not made so much as a reference to the previous night, she didn't ask where he had been, and he didn't tell her. He looked lean and refreshed, she thought. One would never guess he had been out half the night. Though she didn't know the exact time he'd come in, she speculated that it must have been about midnight and not in the early hours of the morning. No one could look so disgustingly refreshed after staying out all night. She put down her cup, wishing she hadn't fallen into such a deep sleep.

At the sound, he looked up. His gray eyes challenged her, daring her to guess, daring her to ask where he had been, but knowing that was what he wanted her to do she would not give him that satisfaction and lowered her gaze.

Quint folded the newspaper and put it down, then rose, unwinding his lean, muscular length from the chair, and glanced down at Laura. She knew her expression was accusing.

"I told you how I felt," he said evenly. "Nothing's changed, as far as I'm concerned." He seemed to be implying that if she felt something more for him, it was her tough luck.

Something hardened inside Laura. The hope that he would come around was beginning to shine less brightly. The cold, expressionless look in his gray eyes threatened to snuff it out completely. She rose to take their breakfast things to the counter.

"You can ride with me," he announced. "There's no need to use two cars."

"I'll drive myself."

"Suit yourself."

His indifference cut her to the quick. It was worse than contempt or hatred because it was nothing, and she had been so sure there was something.

He turned and left without a word.

The days and weeks that followed slid one into another, almost indistinguishable from one another. After several weeks had passed, the hope that Laura had nurtured began to flicker as if it were going to eventually die out completely. She tried to fan it, to keep it alive and not let anything diminish it further. She continually reminded herself that it would take time, and she tried not to let his coldhearted indifference chip away at the love she felt for him. And she tried everything else she could think of, from tempting his appetite with well-thought-out meals, to drawing him out with lighthearted conversation about people they knew, to finding out about things that interested him.

But each attempt was a dismal failure. He continually shut her out, held her away and disappeared without any warning when the mood struck him. Laura began to feel that she was waging a losing battle. Facing rejection after rejection, when all her attempts to close the gap between them had failed, she finally stopped trying. Hope died, and cold resolve took its place. It was a matter of self-preservation, she told herself, to protect her own now bruised and battered feelings.

But all the time this was happening, his desire for her and hers for him did not diminish. Often in the dead of the night she would sense him climb into the bed after he had been out, leaving yet another dinner to get ruined. In spite of how she felt, as soon as he pressed her into the furnace of his body and his hungry mouth slid down the curve of her neck, she would respond instantly. Her arms would lock around his neck, and her hands would sink into his thick, dark hair, and he would pull her into him with a hungry, almost angry need. They would be lost in each other, dying in that world of iridescent sensation. Then it would be over, and he would turn away, retreating once again into the tough shell that had hardened around him.

One morning as Laura got up, she noticed that she felt slightly nauseous. She walked slowly into the bathroom. After the spell passed, she rushed back into the bedroom, pulled out her bedside calendar and started hurriedly counting off the days. A searing sense of pleasure and astonishment shot through her when she realized that, in all probability, she was pregnant.

She slumped against the wall, holding the calendar out in front of her, still staring at the dates as her brain struggled to absorb what had happened. She did some calculations and realized that she might have gotten pregnant when they had first made love on the yacht. The discovery filled her with a sense of soaring happiness. Quint had cared for her then. He hadn't yet discovered that Connie was her sister. There were no undercurrents between them, and he had made love to her holding nothing back. Perhaps their child had been conceived then, when he had loved her, not simply desired her.

Why hadn't she realized sooner? It was all the excitement, she thought. First Connie turning up. Then the confrontation with Quint. Then the hastily arranged wedding. She had put her lateness down to nervous tension.

She closed her eyes, blissfully hugging the idea to herself. It filled her with a glowing sensation, and she drifted with the knowledge wrapped around her. It was the first warm and utterly contented, peaceful moment she had felt since Quint had come back into her life.

Then slowly the warm glow began to recede as Laura wondered what Quint would say. Would he be pleased? The question made her feel uneasy. It was difficult to know how he would react to anything now, after what had happened. What feelings he did have he never revealed to her anyway.

She moved away from the wall and decided that it might be best to wait for the right moment. Surely it would come. A tender moment when that distant closed expression melted away for a moment and she would see the old Quint again, the one who allowed her to know his feelings. She hoped that Quint would be just as pleased and overjoyed as she.

Laura could hear him moving around downstairs. She slipped into the bathroom and began the morning routine, filled with a sense of inner happiness, forgetting the delicate state of her stomach.

At work later that day, Tina came over for one of her daily chats.

"How are the newlyweds?" she ventured with her shrewd dark eyes focused on Laura's expression. "You look a bit bemused. You haven't had your first quarrel, have you?"

Laura suppressed a bubble of hysterical laughter. If Tina only knew. First quarrel! They had been in a constant state of cold warfare from the moment Quint had slipped the ring on her finger. But she couldn't tell Tina that.

"Oh, I'm just a little bored," she said, quickly inventing an excuse. "We need to go out or away for the weekend. I was just thinking of where we might go. We really should do something special, since we stayed in all last weekend."

"I've got just the thing," Tina announced, beaming at Laura. "They're having a glitzy evening at the country club. We're members, you know. Both my mother and father have been members for years. They're both golf fanatics," she explained, rolling her eyes expressively. "If you and Quint would like to come along, we would be delighted to have you as our guests." She tried to coax a smile from Laura. Seeing that she was making headway, Tina went on eagerly. "The country club dances are always fun, and everybody of all ages comes to them. We've finally talked the steering committee into letting us have some of the latest music. What they used to have was unspeakable and suited only to people with one foot in the grave."

"Thanks, it sounds like fun," Laura said. "We need a night out." They needed a lot more than that, Laura thought wistfully, but maybe this would help to get them on the right track. Meeting new people, relaxing, enjoying themselves, it certainly couldn't do any harm.

"By the way." Tina leaned forward, grinning. "How has he been on holding up his end of the conversation? Is he still into monosyllables, or is he lashing out into sentences?"

Laura struggled to hide a look of embarrassment. How could she tell Tina she was lucky if he said, "Pass the sugar." And in the evening it varied to "Pass the potatoes." And occasionally it was "Where are my black socks?" Quint had honed conversation down to a few sentences a day. He was determined to keep his feelings locked away, and anything in the way of conversation other than the purely necessary he shunned adroitly. In the nights there was only the unspoken, fiery physical need when no words were necessary at all to express what he wanted from her.

"He talks freely when something isn't bothering him," Laura said. She spoke the absolute truth, she realized. Something was always bothering him, and it happened to be her. She then hastily changed the topic of conversation. "How's your sister's baby doing?"

Tina held up her hand dramatically. "He's growing by leaps and bounds and howls whenever he doesn't get his way. He rules the household. I'll show you the latest pictures at lunch. Don't forget about the dance on Saturday night. It's dressy, by the way," she added.

"I'll ask Quint, but I'm sure he'll say yes." Laura wasn't sure at all. Yet she went back to her work with a smile still curving her lips. It was something to look forward to.

That evening she let herself into the condo in a positive frame of mind. She changed into old, faded jeans and a white shirt and began preparing dinner. She lifted her head when she sensed Quint standing in the doorway watching her intently. She smiled at him, but the smile faded instantly at the leaden stare of cool indifference that greeted her.

"Guess what?" she said brightly.

"What?"

He spoke warily, but amiably enough, she thought. That was a good sign. His gaze slipped over her long-legged figure outlined in jeans. Her blood heated up instantly under his slow perusal. He still had the same powerful effect on her senses, no matter how aloof he kept himself and no matter what he did. The thought brought an embarrassing flush to her face.

"Tina has invited us to join her and her family at the country club this Saturday. They're having a formal dinner and dance. I thought it would be nice for us to go. We haven't been to anything like that."

"Do they let in ex-cons?"

Her face blanched at his words. "Unless you go around telling them, no one will ever know," she remarked quietly.

"Well, you won't, will you?" he countered easily. "You're an expert at keeping secrets."

Her expression froze. He never missed an opportunity to drive home the knife. She turned away, tears stinging her eyes.

"Your dinner's in the oven," she said quietly, and started to walk out of the kitchen. Over her shoulder, with amazing calm, she added, "You'll need a tux. It's dressy."

Chapter 10

Who else is going to be at this thing?" Quint asked, walking into the bedroom and stripping off his shirt.

Laura tore her eyes away and concentrated on what he was saying.

"Lots of people. I'm sure you will enjoy yourself." If you want to, she wanted to add, but didn't.

"Glad you think so," he said sarcastically.

Something flared inside her. But again, she didn't say anything. She silently acknowledged that sudden surge of anger, noting that it seemed to be a common occurrence lately. So far she had been able to contain it, hold it in check, but she didn't know how much longer it would be before she would find herself lashing back at him. A part of her was beginning to rebel. It was time he put the past behind him.

Her eyes glittered with pique as she applied make-up with a light touch and sprayed on her favorite scent.

Quint, who had showered in the spare bathroom, had come back into the master bedroom to dress. Barefoot, in the pants to his tuxedo, he indolently buttoned his shirt, his gaze following her with a predatory gleam. Laura slipped out of her robe with unhurried movements and stood in bikini briefs with high-cut French sides and a matching lacy bra. She picked up her velvet gown, loving the luscious feel of it as she hugged it against her bare skin. After she had eased into it, she began to struggle to zip it up at the back. The bodice fit like a glove, and she had to suck in her breath. She spoke to Quint over her shoulder.

"Would you give me a hand?"

She felt the zipper rising slowly. His hands slid to her waist and she started to pull away, but he refused to let her go, and a heavy sensuality suddenly swirled between them, like a thick morning mist, when he drew her back against his lean length. Color marched up her bared shoulders and neck.

"There's no time," she murmured softly over her shoulder as she felt his lips caress the curve of her neck. He released her reluctantly.

There was no reply, and he turned away and walked toward the full-length mirror to finish buttoning his shirt while she bent to put on her matching pumps. At the dresser, she opened the lid of her jewelry box. It was a meager collection, but she did have a tiny gold locket with beautiful scrollwork on it that her mother had given her. It was something she treasured, and she lifted it out and fixed the delicate gold chain round her neck, thinking that it would look good with the stark simplicity of the gown. Then she turned this way and that to survey herself from all angles.

She had never looked so sophisticated. Marriage had added a new dimension to her femininity. The black velvet gown showed off to perfection her honey-colored skin, still glowing from the days spent in the Keys. Her upswept hairstyle drew attention to the delicate line of her jaw, chin and graceful neck, and the tiny golden locket, nestled between her collarbones, was a charming touch.

She found Quint staring, and in turn she gazed back at him. Her green eyes surveyed him slowly from head to foot. His dark good looks, dusky skin and amazing gray eyes contrasted with the elegant simplicity of the evening clothes that outlined his lean masculinity, underscoring it without diminishing it in any way. He was breathtakingly good-looking, but not in a pretty way. She felt her blood run hot. Tearing her gaze away she picked up a matching clutch.

"I'm ready," she said, and prayed silently that this evening would be a step toward drawing them closer together.

The country club, which was really a golfing club, sat astride rolling expanses of greens and, surrounded by pines and palmetto palms, was beautifully landscaped. The main building was a rambling structure of timber, with large expanses of glass. Cars choked the approaching roads, wraparound driveway and the adjoining parking lots.

The balmy evening greeted Laura and Quint when they stepped out of the car and walked to the main entrance. There they were greeted by several people stopping to chat and exchange hellos as they made their way into the banquet room and nearby game room that had been turned into a ballroom. The band was already warming up, playing a medley of light music. Laura glanced up at Quint and saw he wore the closed, shuttered look that dominated his expression whenever he was around her. He was like a restless, wary, caged animal. A longing surged inside her, an intense longing for those laughing eyes and the easygoing humor that she had glimpsed only in brief snatches during those few golden moments before he had discovered the truth. If only Connie hadn't turned up, Laura thought distractedly as they made their way through the crush of guests. If only... but she knew eventually it would have happened. Sooner or later something would have tripped her up.

Laura turned at the sound of Tina's voice as her friend rushed up, dazzling in red chiffon. "I'm so glad you could come," she said. Her dark eyes and hair made the perfect contrast to the scarlet off-the-shoulder gown that swirled around her ankles to display red satin pumps.

Tina led them to the banquet room, which was filled with circular white tables surrounded by people in glittering evening clothes. The music from the band drifted in from the adjoining room.

"We're all sitting over there." She pointed.

Across a sea of heads, Laura saw a group of young men and women. Wending their way through the tables Laura, Quint and Tina finally managed to sit down. Laura found herself next to a tall, blond man with twinkling blue eyes.

"Hi, I'm Josh," he said with a disarming grin. "Ever been to one of these things before?" Laura shook her head amiably.

They took an instant liking to each other. Josh had a way about him that instantly won one over, Laura thought. He wore a white dinner jacket that, unbuttoned, revealed a pleated spotless white shirt and black cummerbund around a trim waist.

Laura cast a brief sideways glance at Quint whose enigmatic expression was changing to one of lingering interest as he noticed the curvaceous redhead next to him, who appeared to be slowly oozing out of the top of her gown. Laura felt something remarkably like jealousy sear through her and lowered her gaze to her lap, pretending to fasten the clasp on her clutch bag.

White-jacketed waiters began to circulate among the tables asking the guests what they wished in the way of wine and for an entrée. Once orders were given, the conversation took off, mainly because most of the people around the table were of the same age and unattached. It was all remarkably affable and lighthearted. Tina made rapid-fire introductions, throwing in bits of information about everyone.

"Are you a member?" Josh enquired. His blue eyes twinkled at Laura.

"We're guests of Tina's. I know her from work at Cranston's."

"I call her the Latin American firecracker. She sizzles. Don't you agree?"

Laura smiled at the description and then glanced sideways and saw Quint engaged in lazy conversation with the redhead. There was a smile on his face that irritated Laura intensely. There were few smiles for her, but he managed to scrape one up when he was near a total stranger. She fumed inwardly, feeling the last shred of desire to please him fading rapidly.

"My husband is a pilot. Do you ever fly?" she asked Josh.

"So happens that I do at weekends. I play golf, do you?"

"No." She smiled mischievously. "But I do dance."

Josh's eyes gleamed with amused interest. "Will your husband mind?"

"I don't think so." Quint was laughing at something the redhead had said. The sound of his laughter almost made Laura flinch.

"I'd better not push my luck. I'll ask him," Josh murmured, and rose from his chair.

Laura watched as Quint turned his dark head, to look at Josh with hostility barely disguised beneath a veneer of social politeness. He was going to ignore her, Laura thought, but he didn't want anyone else to pay attention to her.

"I'd like to dance with your wife, if that's all right with you," Josh said with debonair charm.

Quint murmured some almost inaudible reply, his gaze flickering over Laura and then back to the redhead.

Josh turned to Laura.

"I think it's okay," Josh said, "but he didn't look too happy about it." Laura tried to smile, but it was a strain after the way Quint was behaving.

"Come on, then," Josh said. They rose from the table and made their way out to the dance floor in the adjoining room. The band was in full flow, and the sophisticated medley of music had been replaced by a succession of recent rock hits.

"Do I detect a little marital friction?" Josh's eyes twinkled mischievously again.

"To be honest, it's more like cold war."

He was a good dancer, Laura thought idly, as he pulled her into his arms and they moved around the floor in a slow dance. She deliberately put her arms around his neck and let him hold her close.

"Getting even or just trying to teach him a lesson?" he murmured in her ear.

Laura's eyes widened. She hadn't realized she was that transparent. "Neither. I'm simply going to enjoy myself." A reckless surge took her in its grip. "Do you mind?" she asked playfully. She had to tilt her head back slightly to catch his expression, since he was so tall.

"Not a bit." He grinned. "Maybe he needs something to think about."

She laughed as he swung her around and the music plunged into a reggae beat. Suddenly she felt light-hearted and euphoric and the evening seemed filled with fun. She happily put Quint out of her mind, as if she had put on blinkers. Tired of trying to please him when he was being impossible, she decided to enjoy herself and forget that he was there. A little voice nagged at her that this was not wise, but she paid it no heed.

After several dances, she and Josh returned, a bit breathless, to the table. Tina looked up at them speculatively, raising an enquiring eyebrow.

The evening began to gather steam as dinner was served. Josh launched into a long, funny story, and consequently, Laura didn't notice the dark looks Quint cast in her direction from time to time. When she did happen to turn his way, she noticed that the redhead had lost no time in dragging Quint out on the dance floor.

"Miss Silicone Valley has her sights set on your silent wonder," Tina whispered into Laura's ear. "Are you going to let her encroach on your territory?"

"That's up to Quint. He's a big boy." Laura watched them, glued to each other, on the dance floor. She felt bruised.

"Yes, quite a healthy one, too, from the look of things," Tina drawled dryly. "He seems to be responding in a completely normal way."

"Who is she with? Is she with anyone?" Laura was almost afraid to ask, thinking of Quint's nocturnal excursions when she didn't know where he was.

"She's going to be with your husband, looks like."

"Who is she?"

"I believe she's someone's errant child. An army brat, probably some retired colonel's daughter. Most of the people around this table are offspring of the members." Tina bent forward and murmured, "Some of them come with dates, but don't necessarily leave with them. Some of them even have that understanding when they arrive. Take her, for instance. Her date is over there, I think." Tina indicated a dark-haired young man engrossed in conversation with a brunette. "She knows he's going home with whomever he likes, and so is she. Judging from the look in her eyes, she has high hopes for your husband."

Tina moved away. Josh leaned forward and repeated Tina's observations. He couldn't help hearing, sitting so close.

"What do you think about that?" he asked.

"I doubt he'll give her a tumble. He's probably only doing it to be irritating, getting back at me for dancing with you," Laura said with a false show of bravado.

Josh tipped his head to the side and cast a doubtful look at Quint and the redhead. "If you say so," he replied.

Laura glanced furtively in the same direction and knew that Josh's skepticism was not unfounded. She didn't know what went on in Quint's head, and she wasn't at all sure what he might do. She only knew that, although he had rejected every overture she had made to put things right between them, it cut her to the quick to see him with his arms around another woman. But instead of suffering in silence tonight, she felt rebellious, and something perverse surged inside her. Though she tried to stamp it out and told herself it was sheer folly, the rebellion that was flaring inside her could not be repressed, and though she knew no good whatsoever could come of it, she felt herself succumbing to it.

As the evening progressed, those feelings became increasingly more difficult to hide, and the mood that had infected her had transmitted itself to Quint. With a cold assessing look in his gray eyes, he struck back with calculated intent. He encouraged the flaming redhead with lazy sensual charm and cut in when she was dancing with Josh. In fact, he was glued to Miss Silicone Valley.

Laura tried hard to be sophisticated and blasé, but it was foreign to her nature to play brittle games of one-upmanship where love was concerned. She felt her composure begin to develop some serious cracks in it.

Her tremulous pride was taking a severe battering. Her emotions, already bruised after weeks of rejection, rose up in havoc.

Suddenly the atmosphere in the rooms, pulsating with the heat of many bodies, seemed to be stifling, and the rising crescendo of voices fueled by the consumption of alcohol grew deafening so that Laura developed a pounding headache. The infectious tempo of the music that before had produced a temporary state of euphoria and lured her out onto the dance floor now sounded discordant and loud. The whole evening seemed to take on a nightmarish note.

Josh looked down at her as they moved together on the packed dance floor.

"He's coming on pretty strong with Miss Silicone Valley."

"I know," Laura said wearily as defeat crept into her voice. It was poignantly clear who loved whom, she thought dismally. She couldn't keep up this charade of gaiety, this sophisticated plunge into tit-for-tat flirtation. She was too thin-skinned and didn't have the toughness necessary to indulge in such dubious adult games.

"He strikes back forcefully," Josh observed dryly.

"I know," Laura agreed. "He stopped turning the other cheek a long time ago. It's what he usually does."

Laura couldn't understand Quint's behavior. It confused her. He continually rejected her overtures of affection, acting as though he wasn't interested, yet when she paid anyone else the slightest bit of attention, he retaliated swiftly and sharply. It didn't make any sense.

"He's crazy if he doesn't appreciate you. Or blind," Josh whispered in her ear. "I would appreciate you like mad."

He was flirting outrageously, but the words felt like a balm to her staggering confidence and bruised feelings. She looked around and couldn't see Quint. The awful specter of him leaving with that redhead loomed immediately. He wouldn't go that far. Would he? she wondered gloomily. Suddenly tears stung at the backs of her eyes as she came to the swift conclusion that he would. All the stinging rejection and the continuous denial by Quint of any expression of his emotions over the past weeks swamped her. The last remnants of her composure disintegrated.

Seeing her visible distress, Josh bent forward. "Can I help, Laura?"

"Please don't misunderstand," Laura said, hoping he wouldn't take this as some kind of provocative invitation. "But can you give me a lift home? I don't want to stay any longer," she added on a wobbly note.

"Of course, I will. I promise to be a gentleman and not take advantage." He displayed sharp perception and quiet winning charm.

Laura rose and went to explain the situation to Tina.

"You're crazy as a loon, Laura, to walk off and leave her a clear field," Tina remarked.

"I'm not staying and making a scene. When Quint comes to his senses, he'll find me at home. Tell him that, if he bothers to ask. Josh is taking me home. Do you think I can rely on him to behave?"

Tina's mouth curved into a reassuring smile. "Josh is an old friend of the family. We grew up together.

He's a gentleman, and you're in good hands,'' she re-assured Laura.

Laura responded with a weak smile. She picked up her clutch bag from the table, and she and Josh threaded their way through the still-crowded banquet room, where people dawdled over coffee and brandy. As they made their way to the hallway, Laura felt like digging a hole and crawling into it, licking her wounds and never coming out into the glare of light again. The evening had been an unmitigated disaster.

She followed Josh down the long hallway. Loud music and voices drifted after them, as if haunting them. Josh put a reassuring arm on Laura's. It was a comforting gesture. Laura appreciated the kind intent and was thinking what a genuinely nice person Josh was when suddenly a deep, compelling voice halted them both.

''Where do you think you're going with my wife?'' Quint's voice was deceptively lazy, but it still made all Laura's reflexes leap. She spun around and saw him standing there with a quietly murderous gleam in his eyes. The same slight aggression hovered around his lean ranginess, as if he were about to spring at someone or something. He had exactly the same look in his leaden gray eyes that she had seen in the alleyway the night they went to the club, and it frightened her. She stood transfixed, and Josh sensed her apprehension immediately.

Josh confronted Quint, but he was marvelously in control of himself and his natural grace and easy-going charm remained undaunted. He answered without being diminished in any way.

"I was taking her home, friend, since you seemed to be preoccupied with someone else," Josh explained.

"You've got thirty seconds to disappear, *friend*." Quint's voice was low-pitched and without emotion, flat and deadly calm, like the eye of a hurricane before the storm passes over.

Very wisely, Josh stepped aside, raising one hand in the air in a placating gesture. "I was only taking her home. Nothing underhanded intended. She asked me to take her home."

Quint gazed at him with cynical disbelief shadowing his eyes. But he said nothing, as if Josh's words weren't worthy of response. He continued watching as Josh turned to address Laura.

"It was nice meeting you, Laura. Good night," he said quietly, then strolled away, his debonair charm still intact.

Laura stared after him briefly and then she turned to Quint, her green eyes flashing defiantly. "Of all the—"

Quint didn't let her finish. His hand shot out and seized her upper arm, propelling her through the entrance and out into the balmy evening. The sky overhead was spangled with stars, Laura noticed vaguely as Quint practically frogmarched her to their car.

In the same deadly calm voice that he had used to Josh, he spoke to her. "Get in." His low tone vibrated in her ears with compelling force. She remained rigid, and his large hand shoved her inside as if she were a recalcitrant child that he was taking home from some social setting where it had disgraced itself.

She seethed silently as he slammed the car door and walked around to the other side. Where did he get off playing the outraged husband when he had been behaving outrageously with that redhead all evening?

Without looking at her, he climbed in and turned the ignition key. The engine turned over, and the car surged out of the circular driveway, leaving a spray of gravel behind it. Quint tore down the road as if he were flying a plane and not driving a car at all.

"Slow down!" she yelled. He pressed his foot down and raced through a red traffic light.

"Do you want to get us killed?" she cried hysterically. "Do you want to end up in jail for manslaughter again?" The words were torn from her before she could control them. "I'm sorry," she faltered. "I didn't mean that."

Although he slowed down considerably, he still drove at a fast clip the rest of the distance home, his grim expression never altering.

The tires screeched as the car swept into the driveway of the condominium. In a cold, wordless rage, he got out of the car, slamming the door behind him. Laura didn't look at him as he towered over her. Inside, she didn't linger, but walked straight up to their bedroom and began fumbling with the zip at the back of the velvet gown. She heard him coming.

With a brisk flick of his hand, the zipper went sailing down, and the back of the gown split in two, parting ways so that her hands had to support the front of it, clutching it to her bared bosom. She started to move away, still not looking at him, but his hands seized her bare shoulders, and he spun her around. She met his jeweled gray eyes. The lean tapering masculine chin

thrust down at her as he struggled to hold in check
seething emotions. He towered over her, and his body
seemed to pulsate with outraged male pride, which
both surprised and confused her.

"Don't ever do that to me again, Laura," he
warned in a voice that was low and controlled but vibrated with soft menace. "What did you think you
were playing at?"

"I don't know what you mean," she countered
loftily.

"You know damned well what I mean," he
snapped, his eyes furious in an incredibly sensuous
face. "Leading on that smooth-talking parasite all
evening. And don't tell me you were discussing the
state of the economy with him. There's nothing wrong
with my eyesight. I don't like other men sniffing
around my bone. If I ever see anybody taking you
home again, I'm telling you here and now I won't be
responsible for my actions."

She glared at him in disbelief. His bone! How dare
he! How dare he ignore her, only turning to her to
satisfy some physical urge, barely speaking to her most
of the time, disappearing at night; and now because
she had received a little male attention that was not
coming from him, how dare he fly into a black rage,
when he acted as though he couldn't even *see* her most
of the time. She flew at him, all caution thrown to the
winds.

"*You had disappeared somewhere!* Presumably to
help that redhead the rest of the way out of her dress.
I find it hard to understand why you would care what
I do." She laughed on a bubble of rising hysteria.
"What I do doesn't affect you, simply because you

have no feelings left that I'm aware of. You conveniently locked them away when we got married. If you recall, Josh asked for your permission to dance with me in the first place. I only asked him to take me home because you seemed preoccupied with that...that... woman." Laura's defiance only added to the blistering heat rising between them.

Quint suddenly hauled her toward him, his hands biting with bruising intensity into the soft skin of her upper arms. He wanted to say something but she could see that he was struggling with himself not to say it, as a small muscle jumped along the side of his jaw. His lean, taut features grew more implacable, if that were possible. Then he gave a swift, sardonic flash of a smile.

"For your information, she left with her date, and I went to the men's room."

Laura's face blanched. She had been so sure that he had left with the redhead.

"Let's get something straight. You belong to me exclusively. I'm not getting in any line at your door."

His words dragged up more of the seething anger inside her from the reservoir where it had been accumulating for weeks.

"I'm not your bone, and I'm not your whore," she whispered defiantly. "And I'll thank you to remember that! I'm not someone you can conveniently put aside and then take out when you have some physical urge." She started to sweep past him, but he caught her.

"I don't recall you refusing any of my physical urges," he taunted as his voice dropped softly. "I don't remember any complaints when you were in my bed.'' He dragged her back to him and pulled her into his arms to kiss her while she twisted in vain. He molded her to him, and they were pressed urgently together, straining to get closer. A fervor invaded their kisses and began to consume them.

In the week that followed, Laura tried to stay aloof in mind and spirit. She moved her things into the spare bedroom. She made no more attempts to win him over. She decided he had to come around of his own accord. It was something that had to come from him. There was a time when one had to put the past behind him. When that notion would come to Quint's conscious mind, she didn't know, she reflected sadly. But she knew that it had to or there would be no hope for them. Or their baby.

Work helped her to keep her balance emotionally, but her thoughts returned again and again to Quint, and she wondered if there had been anything she had overlooked, something she could have done, some other explanation she could have made or words she could have said. But nothing came to mind. As far as she knew, she had tried everything she could think of, and none of it made any difference.

Aware of Laura's preoccupation, Tina was concerned about her.

''Well,'' Tina said, perching on her usual spot on Laura's desk.

''Well, what?'' Laura asked.

''How are things since the dance at the country club? Tell me to be quiet if you think I'm overstepping the bounds of friendship.''

Tina was a good friend, but Laura didn't want to talk at length about her married life. It made her uneasy.

"Things are a bit cool at the moment." If she were completely honest, *arctic* would have been a better word, she thought.

"Are you speaking?"

"Just," Laura admitted.

"Good grief. Two-Words is down to one or maybe none at all. How do you communicate with each other?"

"We don't, unless we're forced to." And we're sleeping in separate bedrooms, she could have added, but would have found it embarrassing mentioning that even to Tina, with whom she'd always been fairly open and relaxed.

"I think I get the picture. The big chill in *every* situation." Tina leaned over and patted her hand. "Take my advice and don't worry. It will all blow over."

Laura didn't say anything. From the looks of things, it was not going to blow over. This wasn't just another newlyweds' tiff. But she couldn't tell Tina that, so she smiled bravely, and Tina slipped off the edge of the desk, announcing, as usual, that it was time she did some work.

Laura was going through the files, getting something out for Mr. Barnes, when she happened to see Quint's personnel file. For some inexplicable reason, she pulled it out absentmindedly and glanced at it, as if it brought her closer to him somehow. As if it somehow closed the painful gap that was growing ever wider between them, a gap she seemed powerless to close. Her gaze traveled over the familiar typed page of his application form and suddenly stopped at his birth date. His birthday was only a few days away.

A smile curled the corners of her mouth at the discovery. She would get him a present. Something that would really please him. And she would bake him a cake. She had discovered that he had a fondness for chocolate cake. Optimistically, she slammed the file drawer closed and turned around. But what on earth could she buy that would really please him? It was going to take some thought. She went back to work and kept the idea tucked away in the corner of her mind.

At the end of the day, she drove home in the rush-hour traffic still trying to come up with something. She had noticed that his wardrobe was well supplied. He really wasn't lacking for anything, so she dismissed clothing. She thought of his various flying jackets and remembered vaguely that one was beginning to show signs of wear and tear. Yet he had several almost-new ones.

On an impulse she stopped at a bookshop and asked the clerk what they had on aviation. He showed her a marvelous thick volume covering the development of the airplane from its invention up to modern times. The book was beautifully bound, the illustrations were lavish and the history of man's adventure with aviation was written in a style that was intellectually stimulating and jam-packed with information. She couldn't imagine Quint not liking it. Even a man well-acquainted with the development of the airplane would find it engrossing, and she had noticed that in the evenings he often read material related to flying and manuals on airplane engines. She decided to buy it, paid the exorbitant price and left, pleased with her purchase.

Chapter 11

When she arrived home, Quint was already lounging in front of the television, watching the evening news. She walked into the room to say hello.

"I'm sorry I'm late, I had some last-minute shopping to do." His gaze swept over her. "Have you eaten anything? I was just going to make something for myself."

"No," he replied, getting up from the overstuffed sofa and walking toward her. She turned away and started toward the kitchen when his words made her steps falter. "How much longer are you sleeping in that spare room?"

Her steps slowed, and she paused before she answered him. "Until you start acting like a human being."

"What's that supposed to mean?"

"I think you know what I mean," she retorted over her shoulder, and went the rest of the distance into the kitchen.

Laura stood showering later that evening. Her head was tipped back. She had been standing with her eyes closed, enjoying the wonderful sensation of warm water pelting down on her skin. Finally she opened her eyes and turned off the water. She happened to look through the steamy glass door and saw Quint coming into the bathroom. She slid back the door to the shower cubicle and stepped out hastily, reaching for a towel, but his lean, rangy frame barred her way, and with one of his devastating sensual smiles, he snatched up the towel and held it up, out of her way.

"Give me that." Water streamed down her face and soft curves. She reached for the towel again, and again he held it silently and tantalizingly out of her reach. "Give me the towel," she cried.

His gray eyes traveled over her silently, with lingering, insolent inspection.

"Come and get it," he murmured huskily. "It's been over a week since I touched you." She started to rush past him, but he seized her and stopped her. Water was still streaming down her smooth, soft skin, but he was heedless of it as he brought her close to him so that she was pressed against the material of his opened shirt. She moaned helplessly.

"This won't solve anything."

"It will solve one thing," he said roughly, and pulled her close as his mouth captured hers with a hungry insistence and his arms tightened around her, drawing her close against his powerful body, his hipbones and lean thighs pressing into her.

A sigh escaped from her mouth; she couldn't contain it. It felt so good to be in his arms again. They clung to each other, kissing hungrily, voraciously.

Quint broke off the kiss and murmured in her ear. "I'm not going to bed alone tonight." Then he effortlessly scooped her up and carried her into the bedroom, and they fell onto the bed. She clung to him, twining her legs with his, kissing him back deeply as his hand slid over the still-damp surface of her skin. When they had finished making love, he wrapped one arm possessively around her body, and she slept curved into his warmth.

On Saturday when Quint was at Cranston's talking over flight rescheduling and last-minute cargo changes with Mr. Barnes, Laura delved into the cupboards and got busy on the chocolate cake. She had already wrapped the book and hidden it in the cupboard underneath the stairs. She baked the cake and then opened all the doors to get the aroma of baking out of the house so that Quint wouldn't guess what she had been up to when he returned. After the cake cooled, she whipped up the icing and spread the filling between the layers. Then, glancing rapidly at the clock to check how much time she had left, she covered the top of the cake with swirls of chocolate icing and piped on Happy Birthday in mocha. She stood back to admire her handiwork for a few moments before she stored the cake in a cake box.

"Happy Birthday," she murmured when they had finished dinner. He tensed at her words and, in stony silence, gazed at the cake she had put on the table, then at the present she held, as if they were both lethal in some way. Laura's heart began to falter from

its mad dance of excitement. It became instantly clear
that this wasn't going to go as she had hoped.

"How did you know?" he asked chillingly.

"I happened to be looking in the filing cabinet. And
I came across your application, pulled it out and noticed that your birthday was coming up."

Abruptly he rose from the table, as if he wanted to
dismiss the whole thing from his mind. "I don't feel
like cake. Thanks." He had the closed expression on
his face that made her feel instantly shut out. She
could see emotions warring inside him, a tiny muscle
flicking in his jaw. Clearly, her actions had struck
some raw nerve.

"I don't want any more *surprises* from you," he
added. There was a double-edged meaning in his
voice. She knew that he was referring to his discovery
of who she really was. "If you think you're going to
worm your way into my heart again, you're dead
wrong, Laura."

His words left her numb. She watched him turn and
leave the kitchen. Laura stared at the cake and the
present for several long moments, all feeling gone
from her. He had successfully killed whatever feeling
she had, she thought.

She rose slowly, almost mechanically, wrapped the
cake and put it in the refrigerator. Then she walked
away, leaving the gift on the table.

She heard the front door slam, and something inside her snapped. He had gone out again, to wherever
it was he disappeared. It was the last straw. She walked
quickly up the stairs, thinking how nice it was to feel
nothing, absolutely nothing. It was really a wonderful relief, this numbness, after all the emotional pain
of rejection. She pulled out a suitcase and began

packing her clothes. When she had packed all she needed, she carried the bags to her car.

She got into the car and sat looking at the house that had been her home for such a brief time, and then with the same dispassionate efficiency she had used to pack her belongings, she drove away down the busy street. She was not really certain of where she was going, only that she *was* going. She was definitely going away, and she was definitely not coming back.

While she drove, her mind began to work furiously. She would get herself somewhere to live, and she would find another job. She would never let Quint come near her again. She could see that she was fighting a useless battle. He was determined to keep the emotional gap between them, a yawning gulf. She could never accept that, nor would she bring a child into that kind of home.

With all her hopes dashed, she stopped at a nearby newsstand and picked up one of the out-of-town newspapers. Then she drove to a motel and paid the clerk behind the desk for one night.

As she lay in bed in the darkened motel room with only the air conditioner humming in the background, images of Quint flashed through her mind. The first time she had blundered into him in Mr. Barnes's office. The wry grin on his face when he had asked her if she did that sort of thing often. The picnic at Five Lakes Park, when he had virtually dared her to go out with him. Their first date and the first time he had kissed her. The evening at the club when he had retaliated with swift aggression in the alleyway. The scenes filled her with an overwhelming sense of loss. But the images that stood out the most were the sun-soaked days aboard the yacht when Quint had stood silhouetted against the blazing sun like some graven image. And that first time he had made love to her, and the nights that followed. Those memories, illuminated in her mind, were far more brilliant than the others, and as she recalled them in the darkness of the motel room, it was like the sun going in and out of the clouds, elusive and forever out of reach now.

An errant tear slipped from the corner of her eye. She brushed it away, sighing raggedly at the overwhelming love she felt for him, a love that was never meant to be. A cruel fate had twisted their lives inexorably and made sure that it was impossible for their love to exist once the terrible truth was revealed about what she and her sister had done. How could any love, no matter how strong, survive that? She had gotten angry at Quint, but she had really no right. She had told herself that there was a time to forgive and forget. Perhaps there was. But human beings couldn't seem to help how they felt, no matter how hard they tried, and it was pretty obvious that Quint couldn't help how he felt about her. She had become convinced of that, convinced that he wasn't capable of loving her completely after what he had discovered, after trying to live with what she had done. He'd be glad she'd left. After all, he'd gotten his revenge. He wouldn't want her or the baby.

Another silent tear rolled down her face, and she wished for the hundredth time that there was some way she could make it up to him. Finally she turned her face into the oblivion of the pillow, glad not to have to think anymore.

In the morning, she'd decided to go to Connie. Perhaps she could stay with her for a few days until she decided where she wanted to go. She left the motel, stowed her suitcase into the trunk of the car and was soon on the highway that joined the west coast of Florida with the east coast, Alligator Alley.

When she reached the east coast, she stopped at a McDonald's for breakfast and decided to call Connie to let her know that she was coming.

The phone buzzed several times before a sleepy voice answered.

"My God, who is it?" Connie mumbled. Laura could hear her fumbling with the clock.

"It's me, Laura." Her voice floated tremulously over the wire, and sleepy as Connie was, her sixth sense, some fine intuitive thread that held the sisters together through thick and thin, picked up the anxiety immediately.

"What's the matter? You'd never call me at this ungodly hour if there wasn't something wrong. Where are you calling from?"

"I'm at a McDonald's, en route to your condominium." Laura wondered how she would dare to ask Connie if she could stay with her for a few days—she had practically turned her away when Connie was looking for a place to stay. She heard a distant click and knew that Connie was busy lighting up a cigarette, trying to get her thoughts focused.

"What's happened? As if I didn't know," Connie said. Laura had written to tell her about the wedding, which, given the circumstances, she hadn't been able to invite her to. "You and Quint. He's never forgiven you, has he?" Connie immediately zeroed in on the problem. "I told you this would happen."

She had indeed, Laura remembered, but Laura had no more been able to turn away from Quint than she could have stopped breathing.

"That's about it," Laura confessed wearily, not wanting to get involved in any details on the phone. "I'd like to come and stay with you, Connie. May I? I know I have no right after turning you away, but it will only be for a few days until I decide what I'm going to do next. Will it be okay?"

There was a moment's silence in which Laura thought Connie was going to refuse.

"Have you got a paper and pencil to jot down directions? At least he can't find you here," Connie added.

"No," Laura said. "He doesn't know where you are, so it's safe for both of us." She reflected sadly that adversity had thrown her and her sister together once again and upon each other's resources where Quint was concerned. "I'll see you by lunchtime," Laura said after she'd finished jotting down the directions.

The drive to Connie's was a long and lonely one. When she arrived, Connie was dressed and waiting for her, holding open the front door to allow her to pass through into the spacious lounge. Connie asked if she wanted anything, fruit juice or tea or coffee. Laura shook her head and gazed around the beautifully furnished town house.

Connie tossed her hand in a carefree gesture. "My divorce settlement. He was very generous. God only knows why. I was a lousy wife, and I don't deserve it."

Laura smiled wistfully. She wondered if she'd been a lousy wife. She certainly had tried to be a good one. She'd given it all she had, and it still hadn't worked out, she reflected, sinking wearily onto the over-stuffed white sofa.

Connie stared at her speculatively. "So what happened? Pour your heart out. Get it off your chest, you'll feel better." She sank into a lime Queen Anne-style chair and reached for a cigarette, lighting it, watching and waiting as she exhaled. Her beautiful red hair glistened in the bright sunshine that streamed into the white lounge.

Laura began hesitantly. "I couldn't get through his anger. He cared for me at first, but the anger and resentment were stronger." She rose from the sofa and walked toward the patio doors that looked out over the broad expanse of shining river waters. "I thought in time love would win out, that if I tried hard enough, if I was patient enough, if I loved him enough, that surely the anger and resentment would disappear, that the love would be stronger. I was so certain of it. So positive at first. But I was wrong." She turned around with a bleak look in her eyes. "I always thought love was the strongest emotion—didn't you?—stronger than hatred, and that it could win out against all the odds. That it was, indeed, a ruling passion, but I guess I was wrong," she added with a futile, little gesture. "I was so wrong, Connie. If he does feel anything for me, he's locked it away so deeply inside him, he's guarded it and hidden it away so well, that it's invisible. I see no signs of it. Sometimes I don't think he even has access to it himself. Oh, Connie, I love him so, and I can't get through that thick wall he surrounds himself with."

Connie flicked ash from her cigarette and gazed steadily back at Laura, not saying anything for a long moment. "You are a lucky girl, Laura."

"Lucky! How can you say that?" Laura demanded incredulously. "How can you say that when I've lost what mattered most to me in the whole world?"

"You're lucky even to be able to love like you do," Connie said in a soft voice that expressed a hint that perhaps she, herself, had been deprived of that ability.

"*If* you've lost him. Why are you so sure you have?" Connie challenged. "Perhaps when he's discovered you're gone, he'll realize what he's lost and want you back."

"I doubt it. I've tried everything." Laura sank back again on the sofa. "He's capable of desire. Oh, he wants me. I've never doubted that for one moment. But he doesn't love me." Laura described some of the incidents that had led up to her departure. "I couldn't stand it anymore. I had to leave. It's hard living where there is only love on one side," she added finally as emptiness crept into her voice.

Connie smiled with brittle charm. "I know, I've experienced that myself, but in my case it was just the reverse situation." She stabbed out her cigarette. "We were affected differently by our home life. You were luckier, Laura, than I was. It left you with the ability to love. It killed something inside me. In my marriage, Bob did all the giving and I did all the taking. And it wasn't all selfishness on my part. It was an inability to return his love." She got up and walked across the room. "But not everyone is destined to remain that way. I knew Quint before the accident. I remember what he was like. He struck me as a man capable of great tenderness, as well as great strength."

She paced across the room, her skirt outlining her modellike curves, the white, silk halter-neck top displaying perfect shoulders as she swung around.

"My love for Quint was such a long shot," Laura murmured huskily as a sense of loss surged through her. "There were great risks involved, but also great rewards. It looks as though I gambled and lost," she said quietly. "But I've been thinking, Connie. There is something I can gamble on that might be more successful."

Connie frowned in puzzlement.

"The other day I read in the newspaper about a man who went to prison on a charge of rape. Several years later, the victim came forward and said that she had lied. The man was released, and as far as I know, the woman was never prosecuted for what she had done. I don't know all the whys or wherefores of the case, but I do know the man was exonerated, and I think some financial restitution was made to him for court expenses, et cetera." She looked at Connie for a long moment to give added emphasis to her next words. "I want to do that for Quint. I want us to clear his name." She watched as Connie's expression went from a relaxed bemusement to a taut white mask.

"Do you realize what you're saying?" Connie gasped. "There are no guarantees that we will be as lucky as that woman you read about. I could go to prison. I don't know, Laura. I don't know if I have that kind of courage."

"I want us to try, Connie, to do our best to clear Quint's name. To give him back that which is his—the respect of those around him, the opportunity to get the job he wants."

Connie went rigid and said nothing.

"Oh, Connie, we have to do this. We have to do it for Quint. But we have to do it for ourselves, too," she whispered in a voice that had grown husky with emotion.

Connie moved across the room and stood gazing at the river. Laura waited, saying nothing, and the heavy moments of silence ticked by. Her hopes fell as she sensed that Connie was going to refuse to help.

"One time, Connie, I did something for you. Now I'm asking that you do this for me. You owe it to me." Laura waited for what seemed like an eternity before Connie slowly turned around to look at her.

"I can't," she said. "I just can't."

Laura drew in a deep breath. "Then I'll go to the authorities alone."

"You've made up your mind?" Connie said. "He means that much to you?"

"Yes, he does. And he's the father of my child."

"You're pregnant!" Connie seemed to be in shock.

Laura nodded. ' "All right. You don't leave me much choice. I'll do it," Connie said.

Laura moved across the room and put a hand on Connie's arm and murmured a heartfelt thank-you to her sister. "We can explain the extenuating circumstances. I'm sure that would carry some weight with the judge."

The door slammed behind Quint that night as he entered the house. He loosened the top button of his shirt, threw his jacket onto the nearest chair and picked up the evening paper. He hadn't come home the night before or all day. There was an emptiness to the house, something strangely missing. Laura must not be home yet, he thought. That was it. One quick glance at his wristwatch told him that she should be in by now. Where was she?

He tossed down the paper and went into the kitchen. Something on the table caught his eye. It was his birthday present, still wrapped, untouched. It looked forlorn lying there, and he felt a stab of remorse for not even looking at it. Why had he done that? he asked himself. He knew the answer. It was that he didn't want to let her get close to him. He was afraid to, after what she had done. Could he ever again really trust her with his feelings? he wondered for the hundredth time.

Slowly alarm began to uncurl inside him. He walked quickly to the kitchen door, opened it and peered into the garage to see if her car was there. One quick glance told him it wasn't. Maybe she wasn't coming home. Maybe she had had enough. His pulse began to race, and with swift strides he left the kitchen. Taking the stairs two at a time, he charged into the master bedroom. The first thing he saw was the empty dresser. None of Laura's perfume or hairbrushes or cosmetics remained. He strode to the closet and yanked open the double doors, instantly confirming his worst fears. Only a row of his suits greeted his eyes, and empty hangers, disturbed by the draft of air, swung back and forth, seeming to taunt him. His gaze scanned the equally empty shelves above where her suitcases had been stored. They were gone. She was gone.

Stunned, he stepped back. Then with a quick, sharp movement, he flung the closet doors closed again. He muttered a string of expletives and whispered her name to himself, just once, then stood silently and pensively staring into space. His mind threw silent accusations at him.

What could you expect? You damned fool. You drove her away.

The swift sharp reprimands echoed in his head as he stood in the center of the room absorbing the intense emptiness of the house, coming to the undeniable conclusion that she was gone forever. He had lost her. He slipped his hands into his pockets and leaned against the doorjamb. Was it any wonder? a silent voice inside his head accused relentlessly. It was what he deserved, he thought, still with the grim expression hardening the lean contours of his face, deepening the creases around his mouth, making his silvery-gray eyes go a stormy leaden gray. What did he expect? He wondered how he had been so blind to what was inevitably going to happen. It was a miracle she hadn't walked out sooner. He had ignored her, kept what feelings he had for her locked deep within him, buried so deeply that even he wasn't sure he could get at them anymore.

He pulled out a cigarette and cupped it with his hand as he lit it. Relentlessly he reminded himself of exactly how he had treated her. He had treated her and made love to her as if she were a mistress. Yes, that was a fair description. He went to her only when the physical needs of his body drove him. When he had satisfied himself, he put her away from him again. He needed no one to spell it out for him. He had done it deliberately and methodically so that she could never get too close to him again. It had been his ultimate weapon, his strongest protection, so that she could never muddle his mind with all those confused, conflicting emotions he felt for her. He had never told her how much he loved her or needed her, or how, in spite of his silent ways, he always looked for her. How it made him feel good just to know she was there. How much he liked simply waking up with her alongside him. He had thrown it all away, not letting her know it mattered. Why?

Because he couldn't help how he felt about what she had done. He had let bitterness and his dark anger hide his love from her. He had even hid it from himself. He had been really clever, really smart, he thought scornfully. But he had fooled no one but himself. Because it was only now, now that she was gone, that he was beginning to realize what she meant to him and how much he loved her. Now, when it was too late.

But it wasn't too late, he decided instantly. He would get her back and tell her how he really felt. He had to find her and put things right.

Laura left Connie the following week, knowing that the legal red tape and machinations took time. She and Connie had gone to the State Attorney's Office and reported all that had happened, the true details of the accident, their lies, even their home situation. Now it was up to the police and the courts.

With a lighter heart, Laura went on to Tampa to find an apartment and a new job. Tampa was a rapidly growing city, and she knew there would be plenty of opportunities there.

Connie promised to keep her informed of any legal maneuverings in the clearing of Quint's name and how they affected them. Laura left with a feeling of intense gratitude inside her. What Connie had done took courage. Laura knew that on her part it was only a deep love for Quint that had guided her actions.

By the end of the week, Laura had found a small apartment with a rent that she thought she could manage. She'd also lined up several interviews for a new job, one of them with a major airline. They had advertised for a secretary, and, with her experience at Cranston's, she thought it looked very promising.

She immediately contacted Jim Barnes for a reference and found that she had some explaining to do. Apart from a hurried phone call the morning she'd left, she hadn't spoken to him. He was very understanding and promised her a glowing reference.

Laura begged him not to tell Quint that she had called, but getting him to agree to that was a little more difficult.

"I don't mind telling you, Quint has been walking around here with a face that would make a dead man jump up from his grave," Mr. Barnes said. "Everyone clears a path five feet wide when they see him coming. Let me at least tell him where you are and that you're all right and put him out of his misery. No matter what happened between you two, he has a right to know that you're safe and unharmed. He deserves that much, at least."

Laura considered this and realized that Mr. Barnes was right. "You can tell him that I'm safe, but you can't, under any circumstances, tell him where I am. Promise me that you won't."

"Okay, Laura. I just hope you know what you're doing," Jim Barnes said. He also promised that he would let no one else know where she was.

True to his word, Jim fired off a reference that helped Laura land the job with the airline.

The intense activity of getting resettled was a boon at first to Laura's flagging spirits, because it kept her occupied physically and mentally. It was only at night when she was alone that thoughts of Quint came flooding back into her mind. Trying not to think of him was a losing battle. The numbness had worn off, and now the full realization of what she had lost struck her with reoccuring force. It came in waves. She cried herself to sleep on more than one night and picked up the telephone to call him on many more, but something always stopped her—a sense of self-preservation and a conviction that the same cruel twist of fate that had thrown them together had somehow decreed that they should part.

With a quiet tenacity, she made her way through the first weeks in Tampa, going through the motions of living, coming to grips with her new job, furnishing her apartment, finding an obstetrician and preparing for the baby. Yet, questions always hovered in the back of her mind. What was Quint doing? Did he think of her as much as she thought of him? Was he looking for her?

She had written a long, newsy letter to Tina explaining that she and Quint had parted and that she was making a new life for herself. She sighed, wondering if she had done the right thing. She wished her mind would switch off. She was weary of the endless chain of unanswered thoughts.

Chapter 12

Laura closed the door to her apartment's tiny bedroom and sighed as she looked around the small living room and microscopic kitchen. The apartment's chief attraction was that it was very near her work. There wasn't very much else you could say for it.

It had been her home since she'd left Quint, almost eight months ago now. She made a conscious effort to push thoughts of Quint from her mind.

She walked over to the desk, picked up a letter from Tina and idly flipped through the pages. She had not replied to it yet. She would do that today, she promised herself, glancing over the sheets of bold scrawl that so matched Tina's personality. As she read, an inevitable smile curved her mouth. The letter was newsy and funny and typically Tina, she thought.

The doorbell suddenly buzzed, and she looked up with a frown and put the letter back on the desk.

Laura glanced hastily in the mirror. She was dressed casually in faded jeans and a white shirt, opened at the neck with the sleeves rolled up. She looked clean and wholesome, but it was definitely not one of her more glamorous days, she admitted ruefully. Her hair, which she had pulled back, had managed with a will of its own to spring from its moorings, cascading in errant curls surrounding her face. She had been tidying the apartment, and her face was slightly flushed from her exertions.

She opened the door and was suddenly paralyzed. Quint stood gazing silently down at her, looking darkly handsome, his lean, rangy body filling the door frame. Laura's heart began to pound erratically. She tried to unlock her eyes from his gaze, but it was useless.

"Hello, Laura." His quiet voice had a staggering effect as his sensuous gray eyes slipped over her, exerting an immediate pull on her senses.

"What are you doing here?" she finally managed to get out in a soft, tremulous voice, realizing it was a foolish question, because she really didn't want to know. She just wanted him to go away. But he hovered over her, looking breathtakingly handsome—and threatening. Dressed in a flying jacket that hung unzipped, a white shirt and gray slacks, he looked very much as he had the first time he had walked back into her life in the airplane hangar at Cranston's.

"I don't want you here," she whispered.

"May I come in? Or do we have this conversation while I stand out here in the hall?"

Knowing Quint, he would stand there and let the whole apartment block know what he had to say. He didn't care what people thought; he had developed a tough hide in prison.

He stepped inside and pushed the door shut behind him. The force of his tough, masculine presence seemed to suddenly crowd the small room. He threw his jacket onto a nearby chair and stood looking at her. Laura turned away, keeping her back to him, and murmured a soft plea in an emotionally charged voice, "I don't know why you're here. We have nothing to talk about." Her body trembled from the strong play of emotions his nearness had on her.

"We've got to talk, Laura. Now why don't you just sit down and listen," he murmured in that low-pitched voice that always vibrated straight through her.

She turned away from the window and looked at him. Slowly, something in the air changed between them. Laura watched as his gray eyes made a leisurely perusal of her, from the mass of luxurious golden chestnut curls that surrounded her face, downward over her full breasts, tapering waist and rounded hips, to her long legs and then slowly back up again. His eyes had a hungry look in them. The impact of it was like an electric jolt.

With a surrendering groan, she admitted instantly to herself that nothing had changed between them. If anything, it was even stronger than before, she thought as she felt desire stir deep inside her and re-membered how long it had been since he had touched her. How was she going to send him away? Again, she turned away, desperate to ease the potent effect just his looking at her had on both of them.

"I've got a thousand things to do today," she an-nounced in a thin, rattled voice. "Really I do. I don't

know how you found me, but I don't want you here."
She fought to retain some kind of composure.

Why had he come? Her life had just settled into a
quiet pattern. She had just gotten used to being away
from him. She had just gotten used to going to sleep
without aching to be in his arms, without longing for
that lean masculinity surrounding her soft curves. The
memory had begun to fade. Now he was here, his gray
eyes challenging her to deny what was still there between them. Suddenly everything was chaotic and in
turmoil again, and it was all so useless.

"You ran away. You didn't give our marriage much
of a chance."

How could he accuse her of that? she wondered in
amazement. The accusation only convinced her that
they were poles apart.

"I don't want to talk to you," she cried softly, her
voice holding a plaintive note. "I don't want to turn
everything upside down in my life again." She folded
her arms in a resolute gesture. She saw his mouth
tighten and his head angle downward, his handsome
features hardening into set, taut lines. She gazed back
at him. He towered over her, and the room seemed to
shrink with him in it.

"I've got something to say, and I'm not leaving."
He stepped forward with the air of a man who intended to say what he had come to say, and nothing on
the face of the earth was going to stop him.

A feeling of helplessness swept over her.

"Have we got that straight, Laura?" His voice was
soft, steel covered in velvet.

Her last shred of hope, that she might get him to
leave, withered and died. Her gaze slid over his lean,
powerful masculinity, his thick dark hair that had been

slightly ruffled by the afternoon breeze. There was about him that aura of strength she had noticed when she had first met him. She tore her gaze away, knowing that it was useless to try to make him go. She would have to hear him out. Restlessly, she moved toward the small kitchen. Quint watched her speculatively.

"There's something different about you," he said, "but I can't put my finger on what it is." The leaden color of his eyes changed again to silvery gray.

Laura tried to stem the surge of anxiety inside her. She knew why she looked different, and she wasn't ready to explain what that difference was.

"Would you like a cup of coffee?" His eyes narrowed at the tremor in her voice.

"Yes, I would."

Keep calm, she thought. There's no need to panic. One cup of coffee, and maybe he will be gone.

She moved past him, and his expression slipped into an enigmatic mask while she got some cups out of the cupboard and he stood lounging in the doorway. She felt her skin burning as his gaze slipped possessively over the soft feminine curves he knew so intimately.

"How long have you been living here?" His low-pitched voice invaded the kitchen and curled around her senses like a whip.

"I found it soon after I left...you," she murmured, wishing the kettle would boil and he would go into the living room instead of hovering in the doorway.

"Why did you leave, Laura?"

"I would have thought that was pretty obvious." She turned to face him. "You seemed determined to hate me for the rest of your life."

He bent his head and stared at the floor for a long moment. And then looked up again at her.

"I want you back," he said quietly, holding her gaze.

His words sent a swift, sharp shaft of pleasure that was undeniable. The intensity of it shook her. Why was the pull he had on her still so strong? she wondered as she gazed steadily at him.

His eyes darkened, and he seemed to be struggling with some feelings still at war within himself.

"You came forward and cleared my name, you and Connie. The lawyers contacted me and asked if I wanted to take things any further, to reopen the case. I don't. I'm satisfied. I've been exonerated, and that's what mattered most to me. I don't hate her anymore. I don't hate anyone anymore," he added meaningfully.

"Not me?" Laura murmured softly.

"Least of all you, Laura," he added. There was an expression in his eyes that seemed to send quick, sensuous darts piercing her skin.

"The lawyers corroborated what you told me about your stepfather. I think I really knew deep down that you were telling the truth when you tried to explain what had led up to your testimony in court, but I was too angry, too filled with wounded pride. I couldn't accept that I had fallen so deeply in love with you, so I couldn't accept that what you were telling me was the truth." He paused. "It was a very courageous thing for you to do, Laura. And I think it must have been you. I can't see Connie doing it without a good solid push. Am I right?"

"It was what we owed you, nothing more," Laura said quietly, dismissing his words. "Nothing more. No

one can ever make up to you for those years stolen out
of your life. Connie has been ordered by the judge to
do community service. I wasn't charged because the
judge took into account the extenuating circumstances and my age at the time." She looked up at him,
questioning him with her green eyes. "What will you
do now? Will you leave Cranston's and look for a job
with a major airline?"

"I've come to like working at Cranston's. I'm not
sure what I'm going to do yet. I've talked to Barnes
about buying a share of the business and getting in on
the management side, but we haven't made any firm
decisions." He let his gray-eyed gaze slide over Laura.

"But that's not why I came here. I didn't come to
talk about my career plans. I came to talk about us."
He moved forward.

Suddenly the kettle whistled, and Laura was grateful for its shrill wail. She didn't want to talk about
them; it was all too confusing. She wanted him to go
and to leave her to get on with her life, such as it was.
She picked up the kettle and poured the boiling water
into the waiting cups. She replaced the kettle on the
stove, not looking at him, and then lifted the small
tray and led the way out of the kitchen. Quint followed with that sensual ease with which he did almost
everything. She sensed his assessing gaze sliding over
her. When they reached the living room, she set the
tray on a low table in front of the couch.

"Where are you working?" he asked as she passed
him a steaming cup.

She sank into the overstuffed chair next to the sofa,
careful to keep her distance from him. He sat on the
sofa, stretching his long legs out in front of him for a

moment before leaning forward to place the coffee on the table and resting his arms on his outspread knees.

"I have a job with an airline company." She knew he was stalling, not saying what he wanted to say. His eyes seemed to drink her in, and she gazed at him with a longing that she could no longer conceal. As Laura and Quint gazed at each other, the taut lines of his face relaxed. She went on with surface conversation, avoiding the undercurrents that were racing between them and threatening to overwhelm her.

"Mr. Barnes gave me a very good reference. It was easy to find a job." She rose and stood in front of him, only inches away.

"How did you find me?" she demanded with a thread of exasperation in her voice. "Did he tell you?" She had sworn both Mr. Barnes and Tina to secrecy. She was suddenly angry that one of them had obviously gone back on his word.

Quint stared down at the floor for a moment, his arms balanced easily on his knees.

"Let's just say I found out," he said, looking up at her, his eyes darkening. "I've been trying to find you for months. Barnes wouldn't tell me where you were, and Tina wouldn't, either." His voice flickered dangerously with some nameless emotion, and Laura wondered what it was.

Quint didn't volunteer any more information, and the expression in his eyes grew smoky. His gaze began to travel slowly up over her long legs, enjoying the view the snug-fitting jeans allowed.

She suddenly wished she had on a skirt. The look in his eyes made it instantly clear what he was thinking, and the knowledge made her blood run hot and her face grow warm.

"For God's sake, don't stand in front of me like that." He ground out the words, biting down on each one as he tipped his head downward, averting his eyes. "I'm having trouble keeping my hands off you as it is."

A heat rush flashed through her with such riveting force that she almost winced. Laura turned and walked to the other side of the room. Quint, equally restless, moved to the window near the desk. He stared out for a long moment, as if he were weighing his words before he said them. Laura suddenly realized how much she was still in love with him and that she was sliding down that slippery slope of desire, unable to stop herself, with nothing to grab onto.

"Laura, I love you very much. I want you back. I never knew how much I loved you until you left. I didn't know how much because I kept it well hidden from myself."

She noticed that he said the words as if they were dragged from him, as if they were still difficult for him to say, which only served to give them more impact.

"Because of my anger over what you had done, I couldn't admit to myself how much I loved you."

Laura wanted to go to him, to wrap her arms around him. But some caution, some instinctive reserve held her in check, and she stood poised on the other side of the room, afraid to move. Not quite able to believe her ears. All those weeks and months of living with him had conditioned her to hold her natural responses in check. Too many times she had reached out only to be rejected.

"I don't think I could come back," she said in a soft voice that echoed her doubts, her fear that things might still be the same if she returned to him. She could see something flare inside him at her resistance. He swung around.

"Damn it, Laura! I couldn't help the way I felt. I couldn't dismiss those years that were cut out of my life with a snap of my fingers." The intensity of his emotions fired the words at her across the space of the room.

"Why did you ever marry me if you felt that way?" she asked with a husky tremor in her voice, close to tears but struggling not to let it show.

"I told you at the time," he said flatly. "I couldn't stop wanting you. Don't you remember that day in the condo? I told you, I still wanted you, but I didn't like the way you made me feel. I wanted to punish you. Maybe I thought that in time...the anger would go away." His gray eyes deepened as he spoke. "It's all gone now. I want you back, and I promise things will be different."

His lean, powerful frame still dominated the room. Yet there was a strangely vulnerable look in his silvery gaze that echoed his declaration of love, and it had a powerful effect on Laura's senses. But she still hesitated, she still wasn't sure. She couldn't go back to the way things were. How could he be so sure that he had rid himself of the bitterness? Hers and Connie's confessions had restored his good reputation, but it hadn't restored the time spent in prison or removed the scars those times had left on him. She turned away, still protecting herself with doubts. She heard him cross the room and move close behind her. Her whole being was finely tuned to his presence, so that when his hands slid to the sides of her waist and he pulled her gently back against him, a soft low moan of pleasure escaped involuntarily from her throat. She closed her eyes at the overwhelming sensation of his nearness and touch.

"Oh, that's not fair," she whispered.

"What's not fair?" he asked softly against the side of her face, his lips grazing her temple. "The effect you have on me isn't fair," he added huskily, as his fingers softly threaded through the mass of curls at the back of her head, stroking and comforting. "It's driving me crazy being in this room, not being able to touch you. What do you think it's been like for me these past few months? Lying awake at night remembering what it was like between us."

Laura's whole being instantly responded to him, and she shuddered when his arms tightened around her.

He raised his voice slightly. "Don't you know by now the effect you have on me?" He was falling back on what he knew had never died between them, using the most powerful weapon he possessed. He lowered his head to nuzzle the side of her neck.

"I never stopped wanting you. I never stopped loving you. Other feelings got in the way, that's all." He breathed against her ear as his mouth moved in a searing caress down the length of her neck. "Nothing is standing in our way now. I think you want me as much as I want you. Come back to me, Laura. I need you." His voice was an urgent caress, causing desire to surge so strongly inside her that Laura knew she must try to resist it or she would be lost forever. Her hands locked on his, trying to push them away, but he only pulled her closer to him, and she felt him mold her body to his. She turned in his arms, resisting.

"I'm through with love." Laura's voice caught on a tremulous note. She had failed dismally, and she wasn't willing to try again.

"How can you be through with love when you were made for love?" he countered softly.

"I don't want to hear about loving." She tried to move out of his arms again, but he held her tightly and wouldn't let her go.

"I need time to think," she begged. "How do I know it won't be the same as it was?" Her voice was shaking, with all her senses now fully aroused. "Maybe all those feelings are still inside you. It's only because we've been apart for so long. When we're together again, day in and day out, those feelings will come back just as before. I can't come back now. I need time to think first." She pushed at his hands. "You'd better go," she murmured.

"Are you sure that's how you feel?" His gray eyes contemplated her with open skepticism.

"No, I'm not sure what I think. I need time. I don't know what I feel. Everything is all confused . . . inside my head." She couldn't think straight when he was near her, holding her like this. Her voice was choked and barely audible. They weren't the words she wanted to say, but she felt she had no choice. Now, suddenly everything was havoc inside her. Why had he come back and disturbed the peaceful routine of the new life she had made for herself? It wasn't much of a life, but it was all she had. Frustration surged inside her.

"I wish you'd never come here!" The anguished words suddenly exploded from her. She didn't want to say that, either, but she couldn't stop herself.

At that moment, a tiny wailing erupted from the bedroom, and Laura instantly froze, not daring to breathe. She prayed desperately that Quint hadn't heard it. But his head turned sharply at the sound, and his gray eyes clouded with puzzlement as the sound came again, this time much more loudly and much more clearly.

The color drained from Laura's face.

"What was that?" Quint demanded.

"Nothing." She responded too quickly, and then the wail came again, and she closed her eyes, willing it to stop.

"That sounds like a..." Quint left the sentence dangling in midair, set her away from himself and started to move toward the bedroom door.

Laura rushed after him in futile pursuit, unable to stop herself.

"Where are you going? You can't go in there!" Her voice ended on a wobbly note as he turned to confront her.

"Why can't I, Laura?" he snapped as she caught the full impact of his narrowed glittering gaze. She reached out to grab at his shirt, but came up with a handful of air as he moved out of her reach.

"You shouldn't go in there," she warned. But it was no use. With long strides, he burst into the bedroom, pushing open the door which swung back and hit the wall.

She was behind him, and she watched as he stopped short, staring silently in front of him. The tiny room was papered with teddy bears and furnished with a crib and a chest of drawers bought from a thrift shop. A mobile of monkeys dangled from the ceiling. A rocking chair with a chintz cushion sat in one corner.

But Quint paid no attention to the decor because his eyes were riveted on the tiny, squalling creature in the crib. It was flailing its tiny arms and legs in a fine rage. He stood stock-still, as if he had had the breath knocked out of him, stunned from shock.

Quint swore beneath his breath as if he couldn't believe his eyes. And Laura clenched hers tightly, praying she was caught up in some bizarre dream, hoping she would wake up any second now and find that he was gone. But he moved forward and stood gazing down at the baby in the crib for several long moments. Suddenly he turned around and with the intensity of his raw feelings vibrating in his voice demanded, "What is that? And who the hell does it belong to?"

"I'm baby-sitting," Laura croaked in desperation. "One of the women who works with me..."

His eyes were measuring her intently, and a murderous gleam sprang into them at her words, making her snap her mouth shut. A wry sardonic twist of satisfaction pulled at his mouth when she did. It was no use, she thought. He knew. She could see that. Besides, the baby was going to be the spitting image of him.

He bent forward, lifted the baby out of the crib and held it at arm's length in front of him, inspecting it as if it were some kind of new invention, the first one of its kind ever produced. One of his rusty smiles began to curve the corners of his mouth. The baby stopped crying instantly and looked back at him. They were absorbed in each other. Then, holding the baby gingerly, he turned back to Laura.

"What is it?" he asked in a hoarse voice that conveyed how deeply he was affected.

"It's a boy," she said. "I call him Robert Quinton."

Quint's sensual mouth flicked into a wry grin. He was obviously pleased that he had fathered a son. The baby continued to watch him. There seemed to be an instant bond between the two, both were highly curious about the other, it seemed. The baby put a hungry fist to its mouth and focused hazily on his curious father.

Helplessly Laura watched them, unable to tear her gaze away. Finally Quint looked back at her, and she saw his rusty smile fade. With a narrowed, accusatory gleam in his eyes, he put another question to her.

"How old is he?"

"Almost two months. I've been working and leaving him in day care at the hospital."

"You weren't going to tell me I had a son." His voice was deceptively casual, but she knew it masked a growing anger. He lowered the baby back in his crib, and, much to her surprise, the baby lay quietly, with its tiny fist still clenched in its mouth.

"Why didn't you tell me, Laura?" Quint asked, his voice tight with emotion. "For God's sake, why didn't you tell me?"

"I . . . was going to. I was waiting for the right moment, but it never come. I kept meaning to." The words rushed out of her mouth. She had meant to tell him, she really had. "You had a right to know, of course. But I . . . didn't want to bring a child up with things the way they were between us. After I left, I knew if I told you, you would . . . want . . ."

"You're damned right I would want," he replied with that strange, strangled huskiness in his voice again. "He's my son."

Laura braced herself for another sharp rebuke. But instead of the hard, flinty look in his eyes that she had expected to see, there was something else. She stood waiting. He took a deep breath and finally let it out in a long, ragged sigh. It was as if he couldn't believe what his eyes clearly told him was reality. He looked around the room, then back to the crib and then to her, struggling to absorb the new state of affairs.

"I can't believe you kept all this from me," he explained. The tone of his low-pitched voice echoed disbelief, but also other strong emotions. When his gaze flicked to hers, he seemed a little ashamed and embarrassed. She noted with swift surprise that his whole expression had changed. The closed, distant look had fallen away.

"I guess I can't blame you." He dragged the words out slowly and huskily from somewhere deep inside. Unbelievably, his face suddenly relaxed once again into one of his rusty smiles. He walked across the room and grabbed the tops of her arms.

"God, I want you back more than ever now, and I want my son." Earnestness replaced the smile. "It will be different. I promise. I love you," he said. And then he pulled her into his arms and engulfed her in a bone-crushing embrace, his warm breath feathering the side of her face as he murmured the words close to her mouth.

"You're not through with loving, Laura." Then his mouth moved with a warm sensuality over hers, and he began kissing her, the side of her face, her cheek, her mouth, her neck with that lazy rhythm that always drew a surge of desire from her. His kisses were tender yet insistent and demanded a response as his hands slid down her back and molded her to him.

Unable to stop herself, she put her arms around his neck, and her fingers sank into the thick hair at his nape. In seconds, her mouth was eagerly returning his long, drugging kisses. Her whole body flowed into his lean strength, as their hunger for each other surged up from deep inside. The red haze of desire shrouded them in its mist.

He broke off the kiss and muttered hoarsely in her ear. "I want you so much. God, I've missed you so much. All those lonely nights. I thought I would never find you again. Tina wouldn't tell me where you were. Barnes would bridle every time I even mentioned your name. What did you say to him? I couldn't drag it out of him no matter how hard I tried. All he would tell me was that you were all right. You were all right." He laughed deep in his throat. "But I wasn't all right. I've been driving everyone crazy with my hair-trigger black temper. I think Barnes only put up with me because he knew what had happened between us and because the poor guy is surrounded by females at home and knows the misery they can cause." He pulled away to look at her with tenderness in his eyes.

"And now this latest surprise." He grinned. "It still hasn't entirely sunk in yet that I'm a father. I've got a son, and I have to get used to the idea."

"Are you sure that it's not just your son you want?" Laura ached with love for him and was transfixed by this sudden transformation, but she had to be sure of him this time. She was terrified that the bubble of happiness she was floating in was going to burst. She lifted her hand and touched the side of his face with her hand.

"Can't you tell how I feel about you? What do I have to do to prove it to you. Go down on my knees?" His drawling voice ran over her like a caress. "I came here looking for you first. Don't you remember?" he whispered before he kissed her again, dispelling her last remnant of doubt. When he broke off the kiss, her eyes surveyed his familiar face through a languid mist of love.

"How *did* you find me?" she finally asked. He squeezed her, a mischievous gleam in his eyes.

"I saw a letter in your handwriting on Tina's desk, and I picked it up and pocketed it." He was completely unrepentant and pleased with his ingenuity. "I'm going to have the Spanish firecracker after me."

A cooing gurgle came from the direction of the crib. Laura checked on the baby to find him sucking on his fist and watching them as Quint held her locked in his arms. They both began to smile simultaneously.

"I'll bet he doesn't like being ignored any more than I do." Quint bent his head and bit the soft curve of her neck. He groaned softly and murmured against her ear. "I've been ignored for a long time. You've got a lot of catching up to do."

"He also knows how to get what he wants and is very determined about getting his way," she answered, a smile curving her lips. "Just like his father."

"Smart kid." Quint's hands slid underneath her blouse, and his large body shuddered as they touched her soft curves. "You still haven't answered me," he whispered as he flicked open the catch of her bra. One long-fingered hand covered the fullness of her breasts. "I want to hear you say it," he rasped as a huskiness invaded his voice. "I want to hear you say you're coming back and that you can't stand being away from me any more than I can stand being away from you. That you want me like hell." His voice thickened as his thumbs caressed the sensitive nipples of her breasts, and she closed her eyes with longing.

"I'll come back. How could I stay away after what you've told me?" she whispered. She felt desire curling deep within her. The way he was holding her, she couldn't think straight anymore, and she was having trouble getting the words out, as a hazy mist of sensuality enveloped both of them.

"Does that mean you're coming back with me today?"

His hand unfastened the snap of her jeans.

"I don't think I could stay away another minute," she answered in all truth, as she felt his hand slip inside her jeans and press her intimately into him. He groaned and then shuddered, his breathing disturbed, and a look of languor turned his eyes silvery. He held her away from him so that he could finish what he wanted to say before conversation became impossible.

"When? How soon?" he demanded with a note of urgency in his voice. "I want you to come with me now. I don't want to have to hang around here or wait around in Waverly for you."

That challenging love that demanded everything now soared between them. Their eyes met, and the air crackled.

"All I have to do is notify the people at work that I won't be returning. The apartment's lease will be up soon, so that represents no problem, and the furnishings I can have some charity organization come and collect. They're hardly worth worrying about. There's nothing else standing in our way. Is there?" she asked with meaning, wondering if there were still any dark shadows inside him.

Quint raised his head and looked straight into her eyes. "No," he said quietly. "The past will never come between us again. We've both got too much to look forward to.''

With a look of frustration that testified to his mounting desire, he pulled her back into his arms and whispered against her ear. "If you don't let me make love to you within the next five minutes, I'm going to explode.''

* * * * *

Silhouette Sensation

COMING NEXT MONTH

ONE GOOD TURN
Judith Arnold

One summer in Washington, a wide-eyed optimist named Jenny Perrin had shown Luke Benning how easy it was to believe in yourself, how perfect love could be.

Luke never knew why she'd disappeared from his life or where she'd gone. But he hadn't forgotten the lessons Jenny had taught him, just as he hadn't forgotten Jenny. Seeing her again, Luke had to find out what had happened eight years ago. Was it too late for them?

LOVE THY NEIGHBOUR
Jacqueline Ashley

Detective Jack Spencer had a lot to learn about women. When he went undercover without listening to Emma Springer's advice, she decided to play a more active role.

Jack was pretending to be a male escort, so Emma secretly signed on as a client. She was about to discover just how perilous — and romantic — police work could be.

Silhouette Sensation

COMING NEXT MONTH

GUILT BY ASSOCIATION
Marilyn Pappano

Was Christopher Morgan a spy? His brother had been arrested but had been murdered before he could give away the identities of those he'd worked with. Could Christopher really have been involved?

Someone was quietly investigating and Shelley Evans's editor wanted to know who and why. Would Christopher Morgan talk to a reporter? Would it be dangerous to approach him?

NIGHT SHIFT
Nora Roberts

Cilla O'Roarke loved the nights when she worked as a DJ at a Denver radio station. At least she loved them until the calls started; there wasn't anything nice about death threats!

Cilla preferred to keep her distance from the police, but that was difficult with detective Boyd Fletcher. He was strong, laconic, infuriating and determined to watch over her every second — day *and night!*

COMING NEXT MONTH FROM

Silhouette

Desire

*provocative, sensual love stories
for the woman of today*

JUST SAY YES Dixie Browning
NO TRESPASSING ALLOWED Lass Small
PAID IN FULL Rita Rainville
HARD LUCK LADY Christine Rimmer
THE DADDY CANDIDATE Cait London
SWEET ON JESSIE Jackie Merritt

Special Edition

*longer, satisfying romances with
mature heroines and lots of emotion*

THE GAUNTLET Lindsay McKenna
LIFELINE Sarah Temple
BLESSING IN DISGUISE Marie Ferrarella
MORIAH'S MUTINY Elizabeth Bevarly
IN FROM THE RAIN Gina Ferris
AN UNCOMMON LOVE Pat Warren